Methuen's Monographs on Physical Subjects
General Editor: B. L. Worsnop, B.Sc., Ph.D.

DIPOLE MOMENTS

THEIR MEASUREMENT AND APPLICATION IN CHEMISTRY

DIPOLE MOMENTS

*Their Measurement and Application
in Chemistry*

by

R. J. W. LE FÈVRE

D.Sc., Ph.D., F.R.I.C., F.A.C.I.

PROFESSOR OF CHEMISTRY, UNIVERSITY OF SYDNEY;
FORMERLY LECTURER AND READER IN CHEMISTRY, UNIVERSITY
COLLEGE, LONDON, AND HEAD, CHEMISTRY DIVISION, ROYAL
AIRCRAFT ESTABLISHMENT, FARNBOROUGH

WITH 27 DIAGRAMS

LONDON: METHUEN & CO. LTD.
NEW YORK: JOHN WILEY & SONS, INC.

165548

First Published, March 17th, 1938
Second Edition, Revised and Reset, 1948
Third Edition, Revised and Reset, 1953
Reprinted 1964

3.2

CATALOGUE NO. 12/4007/66

PRINTED IN GREAT BRITAIN BY
BUTLER AND TANNER LTD., FROME AND LONDON

FOREWORD

IN preparing this third edition I have kept before me the intention I had in 1938 with the first, namely, to help an ordinary research worker to make useful measurements of dipole moments and to begin the interpretation of them. Accordingly, the construction of apparatus and details of procedure are described reasonably fully. It is hoped also that sufficient original sources are cited to guide a reader into the 'literature' of the subject.

I take this opportunity of acknowledging my indebtedness to many people: to my wife, who for more than twenty years has shared with me an interest in dipole moments, to Professor E. E. Turner, F.R.S., who first showed me the attractions of stereochemistry, and to my numerous friends and collaborators in England and Australia whose names are mentioned in the following pages. Finally, where my work in Sydney is concerned, I am grateful to Mr. C. Buchanan for his unfailing helpfullness in matters mechanical, and to Mrs. M. Cromack, who with skill and patience has handled all my correspondence and writings on dipole moments and many other subjects.

R. J. W. LE FÈVRE

SCHOOL OF CHEMISTRY
UNIVERSITY OF SYDNEY
May 1953

CONTENTS

(*Note.*—All dipole moment values quoted without specific references may be found in one of the *Tables* cited on p. 132. Where no *unit* is explicitly stated, the '*Debye*', i.e. 1×10^{-18} e.s.u., is to be understood.)

CHAPTER I

DIELECTRIC POLARIZATION AND THE CALCULATION OF DIPOLE MOMENTS

THE DIELECTRIC CONSTANT

THE study of the mechanism underlying the dielectric action of insulators has led, during the last twenty-five years, to a considerable increase in our knowledge of molecular structure. The fundamental measurement is the so-called *'specific inductive capacity'* or *'dielectric constant'* of a material, defined as the ratio, represented as ε throughout this book, between the electrical capacity of a condenser when the substance in question forms the dielectric and the capacity when a vacuum separates the plates. An accurate picture of this property was given by Faraday (1837), who pointed out that particles of matter in an electric field could come into a constrained condition in which they assume positive or negative points or parts, i.e. they could become electrically *polarized* by *induction* and thereby give rise to a field which would partially neutralize the applied field. Thus the polarization of the dielectric by induction causes the potential drop across the condenser to be *less* for a definite charge than it would be in the absence of the dielectric. Alternatively, when its plates are charged to a given potential the capacity of any condenser is *least* when evacuated. The dielectric constants of substances can, therefore, be expressed relatively to a vacuum as unity. Known values range from figures slightly greater than 1 (for gases) up to *ca.* 100 (for most organic compounds). A few materials (e.g. barium titanate) are known for which ε figures of some thousands have been reported.

Some examples are quoted in Table I.

TABLE I

Substance	Physical Condition	Dielectric Constant
Air	N.T.P.	1·000583
He	N.T.P.	1·000074
CH_4	N.T.P.	1·000886
SO_2	N.T.P.	1·009930
C_6H_6	100° and 760 mm.	1·002740
Liquid air	—	1·56
,, He	—	1·05
Benzene	25°	2·2725
Toluene	25°	2·378
Chloroform	25°	4·724
Benzonitrile	25°	25·19
Nitrobenzene	25°	34·89
Formic acid	16°	58·5
Water	25°	79·45

In general, the dielectric constant is sensitive to temperature in an inverse sense. The effect is most notable with liquids, for which the alteration between $T°$ and $t°$ can usually be expressed by

$$\varepsilon_t = \varepsilon_T[1 - \alpha(t-T) + \beta(t-T)^2 - \gamma(t-T)^3].$$

The coefficients β and γ are often negligibly small. (For illustrations, see Landolt-Börnstein-Roth, *Physikalisch-Chemische Tabellen*, 4th edn., Berlin, 1912, p. 1212.)

RELATIONSHIP OF DIELECTRIC CONSTANT TO OTHER PROPERTIES

A number of empirical connections between dielectric constants (ε) and other properties of chemical compounds were claimed in the earlier literature. For example, Obach (1891) had noted a relationship between ε and the latent heat of vaporization, for which 'class' proportionality constants appeared to exist: 6·5 for alcohols, ketones, alkyl halides and nitriles; 25·5 for amines; 31 for aromatic hydrocarbons; and 39·5 for aliphatic acids. Walden later reported that the latent heat of vaporization *at the b.p.* divided by $(\varepsilon-1)/d(\varepsilon+2)$, where ε and d are the dielectric constant and the density respectively *at room temperature*, was for 42 substances 115, with an extreme deviation of 10 per cent. However, exceptions to this rule were numerous (e.g. C_6H_6, 290; H_2O, 553), and it obviously had no general validity. These, and other relationships, are discussed in Kauffmann's *Beziehungen zwischen physikalischen Eigenshaften und Chemischer Konstitution* (Stuttgart, 1920), and Walden's *Elektrochemie Nichtwässriger Lösungen* (Leipzig, 1924).

An interesting treatment of a different type was attempted by Thwing (*Z. physikal. Chem.*, 1894, **14**, 286). Assuming that the atoms and groups of a molecule made specific quantitative contributions to the dielectric constant of the substance in bulk, he advanced the equation:

$$\varepsilon = d(\alpha_1\varepsilon_1 + \alpha_2\varepsilon_2 + \ldots)/M.$$

M is the molecular weight, while $\alpha_1, \alpha_2 \ldots$, and $\varepsilon_1, \varepsilon_2 \ldots$, are the numbers of atoms or groups of the same kind, and their 'dielectric constants' respectively. Values for $\varepsilon_1, \varepsilon_2$, &c., were deduced from an analysis of ε data for a large number of compounds:

$$\varepsilon_H = 2 \cdot 6 \qquad \varepsilon_{OH} = 1{,}356 \qquad \varepsilon_{CH_2} = 41 \cdot 6$$
$$\varepsilon_C = 2 \cdot 6 \times 12 \qquad \varepsilon_{CO} = 1{,}520 \qquad \varepsilon_{CH_3} = 46 \cdot 8$$
$$\varepsilon_O = 2 \cdot 6 \times 16 \qquad \varepsilon_{CHO} = 970 \qquad \varepsilon_S = 2 \cdot 6 \times \frac{32}{2}$$
$$\varepsilon_x = 2 \cdot 6 \times M_x \qquad \varepsilon_{NO_2} = 3{,}090$$

The equation holds remarkably well for many materials (e.g. benzene: $d_4^{25°} = 0 \cdot 8739$; $M = 78$;

$$\therefore \varepsilon = 0 \cdot 8739[2 \cdot 6 \times 72 + 2 \cdot 6 \times 6] \div 78 = 2 \cdot 2721,$$

in excellent agreement with the standard value, $2 \cdot 2725$, at $25°$); for some, it is quite incorrect (e.g. tetranitromethane, $\varepsilon_{calculated} = 104$; $\varepsilon_{experimental} = ca.\ 2 \cdot 1$). It fails to forecast effects due to changes in the configurations of position or geometrical isomerides. Such deficiencies suggest that a correct relation will contain vectorial terms by which the magnitudes can be expressed of certain molecular properties upon whose direction in space the dielectric constant clearly depends. The developments required are the subjects of the next few pages.

INDUCED AND PERMANENT POLARITY OF MOLECULES

Molecules are composed of electrons and nuclei in a state of vibration about certain fixed points in space. At any given *instant* the centres of action of the positive and negative electrical charges may not be coincident and the molecule may momentarily possess a *dipole moment* equal to the product of the charge and the distance of separation. By experiment we are able to observe the *average* dipole moment taken over a definite period of time. For rigid molecules with a centre of symmetry a vanishingly small dipole moment is always found—these are, therefore, called *non-polar* molecules; examples are: H_2, N_2, Cl_2, CH_4, CCl_4, C_6H_6, C_2H_2, C_2H_4, &c. Most molecules are, however, *polar*, i.e. their *average dipole moment is finite*. This quantity is a molecular constant, commonly written as μ; it has the order 10^{-18} electrostatic units (e.s.u.) because

$$\mu = \text{charge} \times \text{distance} = 4 \cdot 80 \times 10^{-10} \times 10^{-8} \text{ *}$$

where electrons and Ångstrom units are concerned.

Both polar and non-polar molecules, when placed in an electric field will become *polarized* by *induction*, in the manner described by Faraday. A molecule can be regarded as an elastic body which under an electrical force will suffer two simultaneous deformations: the electrons and the nuclei will be displaced from their mean positions. Such displacements will correspond to induced moments, m_E and m_A. If a unit field induces moments γ_E and γ_A respectively, then for a non-polar molecule in

---

* 1×10^{-18} e.s.u. is also called a '*Debye*', with D as its symbol.

an electric field F, the average moment $\bar{m}$ taken over all molecules is

$$\bar{m} = (\gamma_E + \gamma_A)F \quad . \quad . \quad . \quad . \quad (\mathrm{I})$$

When a molecule possessing a *permanent dipole* is placed in an electric field it will tend to orient itself so that its potential energy is a minimum, i.e. it will tend to align its moment against the field. This orientative action of the field is hindered by the kinetic reactions of thermal agitation which conduce to an equal orientation in all directions. In consequence, a statistical equilibrium is set up in which a slight excess of molecules have their permanent doublets antiparallel to the field. For the field strengths and temperatures commonly used in dielectric

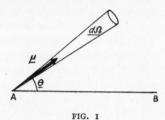

FIG. I

constant measurements the ratio of the numbers of molecules oriented parallel and antiparallel is nearly unity. The slight excess of molecules directed against the field corresponds effectively to a further moment whose average value, $\bar{m}_0$, is also proportional to the field strength. This is known as the *orientation polarization*. It was first evaluated by Debye (*Physikal. Z.*, 1912, **13**, 97). Consider an assemblage of molecules, each having a permanent moment of μ e.s.u. In the absence of an applied field these dipoles will be arranged in a completely random manner, so that the number confined in a solid angle $d\Omega$ and making at any instant an angle θ to AB (Fig. I) is $A \, d\Omega$ (where A is a constant depending on the number of molecules per unit volume). In a field of intensity F, however, a polar molecule acquires a potential energy u given generally by $-\mu F \cos \alpha$, where α is the angle between the dipole axis and the field direction. Suppose, now, the latter to be along AB, any molecule at $\theta°$ to AB will have a potential energy of $-\mu F \cos \theta$, and—according to the Maxwell-Boltzmann distribution 'law'—the number in $d\Omega$ with this orientation will now be $A e^{-u/kT}.d\Omega$. The total number in the whole assemblage follows by integrating the last quantity over all directions in space, namely, for solid angles between o and 2π:

$$\text{Total number} = \int_0^{2\pi} A e^{-u/kT}.d\Omega = \int_0^{2\pi} A e^{(\mu F \cos \theta)/kT}.d\Omega.$$

Since the moment of each molecule in the direction of the field is $\mu \cos \theta$, the moment within the solid angle $d\Omega$ will be $A e^{-u/kT}.\mu \cos \theta.d\Omega$ and the resultant value for all the molecules may again be obtained by integration between o and 2π. Hence the average moment of one molecule in the direction of the field is

$$\bar{m}_0 = \frac{\int_0^{2\pi} A e^{(\mu F/kT) \cos \theta}.\mu \cos \theta.d\Omega}{\int_0^{2\pi} A e^{(\mu F/kT) \cos \theta}.d\Omega}$$

(in which the integration is to be taken over all possible directions). If $\mu F/kT = x$, we have:

$$\frac{\bar{m}_0}{\mu} = \coth x - \frac{1}{x} = L(x).$$

$L(x)$ is the Langevin function of x; it is expanded as follows: $x/3 - x^3/45 + \dots$ However, for the field strengths and temperatures commonly used in dipole moment measurements, $\mu F/kT = x$ is a small quantity. Accordingly $L(x)$ can be considered equal to the first term alone. Thus

$$\bar{m}_0 = \mu x/3 = \mu^2 F/3kT \quad . \quad . \quad . \quad (2)$$

This approximation does not become seriously incorrect until fields of the order several kilo-V/cm., or temperatures usually well below the m.p.s. of most substances, are involved. Hence from (1) and (2) the total average moment exhibited by a molecule in an electrostatic field is

$$\bar{m} = (\gamma_E + \gamma_A + \mu^2/3kT)F \quad . \quad . \quad . \quad (3)$$

To make γ_E, γ_A, and μ accessible to experimental observation $\bar{m}/F$ must be replaced by practially obtainable data. This can be done by using the considerations of Mosotti (1850) and Clausius (1879).

THE MOSOTTI-CLAUSIUS RELATION

Consider a substance of density, d, and dielectric constant, ε, between the plates of a condenser charged with electricity of density, $\pm Q$. These charges cause a homogeneous field of force, F, to act on the molecules (molecular weight M) of the dielectric. In each molecule an average moment, $\bar{m}$, is induced, and since these are all parallel, the moment U induced in 1 c.c. is $U = dN\bar{m}/M$ (where N is Avogadro's number). In the dielectric, there are equal amounts of positive and negative electricity in any space element: only on interfaces do uncompensated charges appear.

If two such interfaces are now made by removing a section between two planes perpendicular to the lines of force, and if the thickness and the surface area of the section be k and A, respectively, then the electric moment of the slice is $K \times A \times U$, i.e. the areas must be charged with amounts of electricity $\pm AU$, of density $\pm U$. If now the slice is taken at an angle, α, with the field, since it has the same volume it will have the same moment and the same total charges on the two surfaces, viz. $\pm AU$, as in the previous case. But the surface area is now $A/\sin \alpha$, and therefore the density of charge is

$U \sin \alpha$. The interfaces where the plates touch the dielectric must be charged with electricity of density $\pm U$ (α being 90°), the charges being opposite in sign to those of the plates themselves, the densities of charge on which are U. The condenser can, therefore, be regarded as an empty condenser charged with electricity of density $Q-U$; hence ε (the dielectric constant) $= Q/(Q-U)$.

F is the electric force which acts upon the molecules; it can be defined as the force which would be exerted

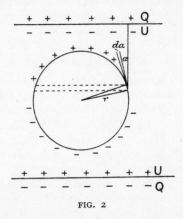

FIG. 2

on a unit charge of electricity situated in empty space between the plates. To calculate this force in the interior of a body, therefore, a spherical cavity is constructed to surround the measuring unit of electricity. The force acting on this unit $= F = F_1 + F_2 + F_3$. These we will consider separately.

F_1 is the force from the plates and from the interfaces between the plates and the dielectric: it will be the same as that acting in an empty condenser with charge $Q-U$ on the plates, therefore, $F_1 = 2 \times 2\pi(Q-U)$. F_2 is the force from the induced charges on the surfaces of the spherical cavity facing the plates. To evaluate F_2 the surface of the sphere is divided up into rings, the boundaries of such a ring being given by the angles α and $\alpha+d\alpha$.

The area of this ring is $2\pi r^2 \cos \alpha.d\alpha$.

Its charge is, therefore, $2\pi r^2 \cos \alpha.d\alpha \times U \sin \alpha$, and hence the force exerted on the unit charge parallel to the field is

$$\frac{2\pi r^2 \cos \alpha.d\alpha \times U \sin \alpha \times \sin \alpha}{r^2} = 2\pi U.\sin^2\alpha.\cos \alpha.d\alpha.$$

The force from the upper half of the sphere is

$$2\pi U \int_0^{\pi/2} \sin^2 \alpha \cos \alpha.d\alpha = \frac{2\pi}{3}.U.$$

This is only half the force; F_2, therefore, equals twice this, namely, $4\pi U/3$.

For F_3, the force due to the material situated *within* the surface of the spherical cavity, no general expression can be given. It is zero for non-associated liquids, gases and cubic crystals.

Therefore, if F_3 be neglected,

$$F = 4\pi(Q-U)+4\pi U/3$$

whence
$$Q = \frac{F}{4\pi}+\frac{2U}{3}.$$

Now ε, the dielectric constant, $= Q/(Q-U)$

$$= \left(\frac{F}{4\pi}+\frac{2U}{3}\right) \div \left(\frac{F}{4\pi}-\frac{U}{3}\right)$$

$$= \frac{3F+8\pi U}{3F-4\pi U}.$$

But the moment developed is proportional to the field, within limits, i.e. $U = (constant)F$. Substitution and simplification gives: $constant = \frac{3}{4\pi}.\frac{\varepsilon-1}{\varepsilon+2}$.

But $U = dN\bar{m}/M = (constant) F$

2

and hence the required ratio, $\dfrac{\bar{m}}{F} = \dfrac{M}{Nd} \cdot \dfrac{3}{4\pi} \cdot \dfrac{\varepsilon-1}{\varepsilon+2}$.

But from equation (3), $\dfrac{\bar{m}}{F} = \left(\gamma_E + \gamma_A + \dfrac{\mu^2}{3kT}\right)$.

The complete expression for the *molecular polarization*, therefore, becomes

$$\frac{\varepsilon-1}{\varepsilon+2} \cdot \frac{M}{d} = \frac{4\pi N}{3}\left(\gamma_E + \gamma_A + \frac{\mu^2}{3kT}\right) \quad . \quad . \quad (4)$$

It may be noted at this stage that by reason of the various assumptions underlying its derivation (4) should be most nearly valid only for gases at pressures such that the constituent molecules are sufficiently separated to exert no mutual influences; nevertheless, experimentally it has been found that it can be applied with fair success—as will be shown later—to dilute solutions of substances in non-polar solvents.

THE DEDUCTION OF DIPOLE MOMENTS FROM MOLECULAR POLARIZATIONS

The quantity on the left-hand side of the equation (4) is generally known as the *total molecular polarization* ($_TP$) of a substance. It is equal to the sum of three terms:

$$\frac{4\pi N\gamma_E}{3}, \quad \frac{4\pi N\gamma_A}{3}, \quad \text{and} \quad \frac{4\pi N\mu^2}{9kT},$$

which are respectively the *electronic*, *atomic*, and *orientation polarizations* ($_EP$, $_AP$, and $_OP$). These may be visualized qualitatively by extending the picture indicated on p. 4. In a molecule both the associations between each atomic nucleus and its electrons, and those between neighbouring atoms, are elastic in nature. Moreover, when dissimilar atoms are bonded together the 'centres of gravity' of their positive and negative charges cease to be coincident—as they would be if the atoms were infinitely separated and the observation averaged over a period of time. In other words the link-age joining them has permanent polarity and the terminal atoms effectively have opposed fractional charges, δ^+ and δ^-. In the absence of an external field all these polar bonds contribute to the resultant mole-cular moment μ.

In the presence of a field, however, a turning force, opposed by thermal agitation, will be exerted on the molecules *via* their molecular moments. This leads to the *molecular orientation polarization*. The field will also cause two further effects. It will tend (*a*) to draw elec-trons one way and nuclei the other—deformations creat-ing induced moments which become manifest as the *molecular electronic polarization*, and (*b*) to disturb the mean positions of the δ^+ and δ^- atoms, or the relative angles of polar links—distortions again producing in-duced moments which in turn are recognized in the *molecular atomic polarization*. The last two processes are temporary and only occur while a field is interacting with a molecule, they will involve, for each electron cloud and nucleus or each valence bond or angle, a 'restoring force constant' having an inverse influence on the polarization concerned.

In order to utilize (4) for the calculation of dipole moments γ_E and γ_A must be evaluated or eliminated. Either of these alternatives is easy to effect once the significance of $\frac{4}{3}\pi N(\gamma_E+\gamma_A)$ is grasped. To this end it can be remarked that for the measurement of the dielec-tric constant an alternating field is commonly employed, and that the observed dielectric constant, and hence the molecular polarization, depends on the frequency of the applied field. At low frequencies the dielectric constant is numerically equal to that obtained when a steady field is employed. This value persists as the frequency is increased until the duration of the field becomes com-parable with the relaxation period of the molecular species forming the dielectric when the molecules are—owing to their inertias—unable any longer completely to follow the reversals of the field. They lag behind it. A diminution in $\bar{m}_0$, therefore, occurs. With further frequency increase, ultimately $\bar{m}_0$ disappears altogether. At this point the molecular polarization equals the sum of the atomic and electronic polarizations. At a still higher frequency, however, the atomic nuclei cease to follow the field and thus a second drop in the polarization is caused. When this is complete only the electronic polarization remains.

This description is summarized by an equation of the following type:

$$_TP = \sum \frac{C_E}{f_E^2 - f^2} + \sum \frac{C_A}{f_A^2 - f^2} + \frac{4\pi N}{3} \cdot \frac{\mu^2}{3kT} \cdot \frac{1}{1 + if/f_0},$$

where C_E and C_A are constants referring to the electrons and atomic nuclei, f_E and f_A are the respective resonance frequencies and f is the applied frequency. It will be seen that as f passes the proper frequencies, f_E and f_A, discontinuities in the relation between polarization and frequency will result owing to absorption, and that—as f/f_0 becomes greater than unity—the contribution to $_TP$ of the third term will slowly diminish. A curve to illustrate these points is drawn on p. 13; the absorption due to the electrons and atoms is indicated in the ultra-violet and infra-red regions (A and B) respectively, and the gradual drop in the orientation polarization is shown in the short wave radio region at C.

Clearly, therefore, $_0P$ could be evaluated for a substance if experimental data on the variation of ε through the necessary frequency range were available. At the present day the bulk of the dielectric constants on record have been obtained with frequencies not much greater than 10^7 cycles per sec. Knowledge of the polarization at the higher frequencies can, however, be attained by the use of a relation due to Maxwell (1881), namely, that for measurements carried out *at the same frequency*, $\varepsilon = n^2$ (where n is the refractive index of a substance). Thus the total polarization can be rewritten as $\dfrac{n^2-1}{n^2+2} \cdot \dfrac{M}{d}$ and is seen to be identical with the *molecular refraction* (R_L) according to the well-known Lorenz-Lorentz formula. For a given substance this quantity is a *constant* very nearly

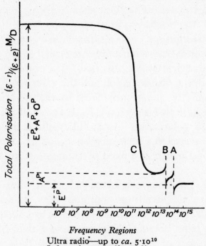

FIG. 3.—To illustrate the dependence of the total polarization of a dipolar substance on the frequency of the field used in the dielectric constant measurement

(because $\bar{m}_0$ makes no contribution to it) independent of *temperature and state*. The most popular method for the measurement of dipole moments is based upon this fact; it is therefore described first.

(1) *The Refractivity Method*. Ideally for this one

should observe the total polarization from density and radio-frequency dielectric constant measurements and calculate the orientation polarization by subtracting the molecular refraction found using infra-red light of a wave-length well removed from any absorption bands. Examples of such refractive index determinations may be seen in a paper by Cartwright and Errera (*Proc. Roy. Soc.*, 1936, **154A**, 138); they are, however, experimentally difficult to make. Workers have, therefore, commonly replaced the somewhat inaccessible $R_{infrared}$ by one or other of the following approximations: (*a*) the molecular refraction for the Na_D line is taken as $_EP + _AP$ and the difference between it and $_TP$ regarded as $_OP$; or (*b*) the molecular refraction is obtained for a number of wave-lengths in the visible region and the value (R_∞) for light of infinite wave-length calculated by the use of an extrapolation formula (see below). R_∞ is accepted as being the electronic polarization alone. The atomic polarization has, on occasion, been neglected, or at other times roughly estimated as a fixed percentage—from 5 to 15— of R_∞.

These practices originated when $_AP$ was thought always to be small—an opinion now known to be erroneous. Of (*a*) and (*b*), the former is less objectionable than the latter because R_D *as measured* with sodium light contains part of the unknown $_AP$, and thus—in work whose purpose is to compare the polarities of a related series of molecules—is likely to lead to more correct relative results (cf. later under 'atomic polarization').

With either alternative a figure representing the orientation polarization is ultimately obtained. Now, since $_OP = 4\pi N\mu^2/9kT$, we have, after the insertion of the appropriate values for the constants (these are conveniently listed by Birge, *Reports on the Progress of Physics*, 1941, **8**, 126),

$$\mu = 0 \cdot 012812 \sqrt{_OP \cdot T} \cdot 10^{-18} \text{ e.s.u.}$$

The refractivity method is unsatisfactory when the moment to be evaluated is less than about $0.4 . 10^{-18}$ e.s.u. In such cases $_oP$ is a small difference of two large numbers, and—being liable to contain the accumulated errors both of observation and imperfect allowance for $_AP$—is an extremely unreliable quantity. If in addition $_oP$ is less than unity the position is worse because the dipole moment depends upon $\sqrt{_oP}$.

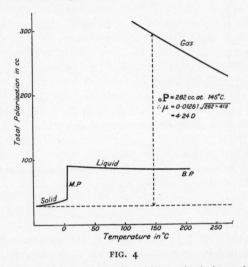

FIG. 4

(2) *Ebert's Method.* Briefly, this method depends on the fact that in gases and, to a less extent, in liquids the molecules are free, whilst in solids they are fixed by forces from the surrounding molecules into positions in the crystal lattice. Therefore, in solids the effect of an alternating field or thermal agitation is nearly nil, and accordingly $\bar{m}_0$ must approximate to zero. This seems to be true at temperatures well below the m.p. (cf. Fig. 4, in which the total molecular polarization of nitrobenzene is plotted against the temperature), where

$M(\varepsilon=1)/(\varepsilon+2)d$ is generally found to be of the same order as, but slightly greater than, the molecular refraction. Thus $_0P$ for a polar substance can be evaluated from the results of dielectric constant measurements on the compound first as a gas and secondly as a solid. This procedure has the practical disadvantage that both the density and dielectric constant of the solidified

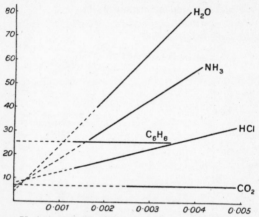

FIG. 5.—Variation of $_TP$ with $1/T$ for a number of polar and non-polar compounds

material need to be ascertained, so that with many compounds a temperature below that of the laboratory is thus necessitated. Even those which are normally solid cause trouble since, through contraction during the setting of a melt, it is hard to fill a density bottle or the test condenser without cracks and interstitial air spaces forming in the mass (cf. Ebert, *Z. physikal. Chem.*, 1924, **113**, 1).

(3) *The Temperature Method.* Since $_EP$ and $_AP$ are not dependent upon temperature, equation (4) can be rewritten as

$$M(\varepsilon-1)/(\varepsilon+2)d = A + B/T \quad . \quad . \quad (5)$$

in which A and B are constants. The former is sometimes called the 'deformation polarization', $_DP$, and is merely the sum of the electronic and atomic polarizations; the latter is numerically $4\pi N\mu^2/9k$. The total polarization of a substance, therefore, displays a linear relationship with the reciprocal of the absolute temperature; some illustrations are given in Fig. 5.

Thus if the total polarizations $_TP_1$ and $_TP_2$ of a substance at the two temperatures T_1 and T_2 respectively, are known, it follows that

$$B = (_TP_1 - _TP_2)(T_1 T_2)/(T_2 - T_1),$$

whence the dipole moment is easily obtained, since

$$\mu = 0.012812\sqrt{B}.$$

Atomic Polarization. This can be estimated experimentally for gaseous materials by extrapolating the $_TP$ *versus* $1/T$ curves back to the point $1/T=0$, for which $_TP = _EP + _AP = _DP = A$ (cf. Fig. 5), and then subtracting the value for $_EP$ ($=R_\infty$) calculated from measurements of the dispersion of the refractive index in the visible region.

A number of formulae exist whereby $_EP$ may be obtained. If n_1, n_2, n_3 and n_4 are the refractive indexes recorded for a substance at wave-lengths λ_1, λ_2, λ_3 and λ_4 respectively, then

$$n_\infty^2 = \frac{(n_3^2 . \lambda_3^2 - n_4^2 . \lambda_4^2)(n_2^2 - n_1^2) - (n_1^2 . \lambda_1^2 - n_2^2 . \lambda_2^2)(n_4^2 - n_3^2)}{(\lambda_2^2 - \lambda_1^2)(n_4^2 - n_3^2) - (\lambda_4^2 - \lambda_3^2)(n_2^2 - n_1^2)}$$

Alternatively, if figures at only two wave-lengths are available, the following may be used:

$$n_\infty^2 = 1 + \frac{(\lambda_1^2 - \lambda_2^2)(n_1^2 - 1)(n_2^2 - 1)}{\lambda_1^2(n_2^2 - 1) - \lambda_2^2(n_1^2 - 1)}.$$

From n_∞^2, by incorporating the molecular volume V ($=M/d$) R_∞ is, of course, $(n_\infty^2 - 1)V/(n_\infty^2 + 2)$ c.c. R_∞

can also be evaluated directly from a pair of molecular refractions, R_1 and R_2, when these have been determined at known wave-lengths, λ_1 and λ_2:

$$R_\infty = R_1 R_2 (\lambda_2^2 - \lambda_1^2)/(\lambda_2^2 R_1 - \lambda_1^2 R_2).$$

The requisite data for these operations are frequently to be found in such sources as Beilstein's *Handbuch*, the *International Critical Tables*, the *Tabellen* of Landolt-Börnstein, etc. Papers by Vogel and collaborators (*J.C.S.*, 1928–48) contain *inter alia* the refractive indexes for over 700 highly purified liquid compounds, in each case n being reported for the four wave-lengths 6563A (C or Hα line), 5893 (D line), 4861 (F or Hβ line) and 4341 (G' or Hγ line). From this large body of reliable information lists of atomic and structural constants, amending those by earlier workers, have been prepared (see especially *J.C.S.*, 1948, 1842, and *Chem. and Ind.*, 1950, 358), thus making possible an *a priori* approximation to R_∞, whenever actual measurements are lacking, *via* the 'theoretical' molecular refractions for two wave-lengths and the third of the formulae quoted above.

The orders of magnitude of the atomic polarizations of a number of compounds may be seen from the table on page 19.

It must be emphasized that $_AP$, deduced in this manner, is inevitably a somewhat uncertain quantity since in most cases polarizations are only available over temperature ranges in which $1/T$ varies from *ca.* 0·002–*ca.* 0·003. The extrapolation of such a $_TP \times 1/T$ curve to $1/T = 0$ will therefore be sensitively affected by small experimental errors in the total polarizations. The case of sulphur dioxide (*J.C.S.*, 1950, 276) illustrates the point: from polarization measurements on this gas at fifteen temperatures between 296° and 444° K. the A term in equation (5) is 10·9±0·6 c.c. while R_∞ is known to be 9·54 c.c. from careful and extended studies of the re-

Substance	R_∞ c.c.	R_D c.c.	$_EP+_AP=_DP$ c.c.	$_AP=_DP-R_\infty$ c.c.
Carbon dioxide	6·59	6·71	7·34 (1)	0·75
Benzene	25·05	26·2	26·9 (2)	1·85
Diethyl ether	22·0	22·5	24·45 (3)	2·45
Di-*n*-butyl ether	40·0	40·9	43·3 (3)	3·3
Methyl chloride	11·3	11·5	13·6 (4)	2·3
Methylene dichloride	16·0	16·4	20·0 (4)	4·0
Chloroform	20·8	21·4	25·3 (4)	4·5
Carbon tetrachloride	25·7	26·45	28·1 (4)	2·4
Chlorobenzene	29·9	31·1	34·9 (5)	5·0
Nitrobenzene	30·9	32·7	36·2 (5)	5·3

Refractivity figures for CO_2 are from Cuthbertson (*Phil. Trans.*, 1913, **213A**, 1), those for the remaining compounds are taken or calculated from various papers by Vogel (see *J.C.S.*, 1948, 1825, for further references). For the distortion polarizations quoted, cf. (1) *Trans. Far. Soc.*, 1947, **43**, 374; (2) *J. Amer. Chem. Soc.*, 1933, **55**, 453; (3) *J.C.S.*, 1952, 1643; (4) *ibid.*, 1950, 556; (5) *ibid.*, 1934, 1094.

fractive dispersion. Accordingly the atomic polarization lies between 0·8 and 2·0 c.c., i.e. between 8 and 21 per cent of the related $_EP$. Similar discrepancies have often been found between the data of different observers, e.g. a review of the earlier literature by Sugden (*Trans. Far. Soc.*, 1934, **30**, 738) quotes alternative values of $_AP$ for some of the compounds in the above list as follows: CO_2, 0·57, 0·69, 1·09; C_6H_6, 1·4; Et_2O, 3·4, 4·0, 4·2, 5·7; MeCl, 1·7 or 2·6 c.c. With modern technique such differences, though lessened, still occur. Almost always they are due to variations in $_DP$, not $_EP$. Some other method for the determination of distortion polarizations is clearly desirable.

It follows from Fig. 3 that $_DP$ should be calculable from the n^2 (or ε) observed using electro-magnetic radiation of a frequency in the neighbourhood of 5×10^{12} cycles/sec. The fullest exploration of this possibility to date has been made by Cartwright and Errera

(*Proc. Roy. Soc.*, 1936, **154A**, 138) with infra-red 'Rest-strahlen' of wave-lengths between 52 and 152 microns (i.e. frequencies from 6 to 2×10^{12} c.p.s.); a few examples from their paper are tabulated:

	$_DP = R_{\text{infra red}}$	$_EP$	$_AP$
Methyl alcohol	10·1	8·1	2·0
Ethyl alcohol	16·4	12·6	3·8
Amyl alcohol	33·8	29·2	4·6
Diethyl ether	25·3	22·1	3·2
Dipropyl ether	35·8	30·8	5·0
Benzene	25·6	25·0	0·6
Toluene	30·6	29·7	0·9
Nitrobenzene	33·1	29·2	3·9
Carbon disulphide	22·2	19·8	2·4
Carbon tetrachloride	27·0	25·8	1·2

The authors themselves comment that the agreement with atomic polarizations deduced from dielectric measurements is not good.

Another source of information, not yet much used, lies in infra-red spectroscopy, and requires the measurement of the absolute intensities of the chief absorption bands of the molecule under consideration. Both the experimental technique and theoretical interpretation are complicated (see Wilson and Wells, *J. Chem. Phys.*, 1946, **14**, 578, Thorndike, Wilson and Wells, *ibid.*, 1947, **15**, 157, and Thorndike, *ibid.*, 868), but for the few gases so far examined a promising agreement is shown with older results obtained *via* the dielectric constant at radio frequencies:

gas	$_AP$ (from i.r. intensities)	$_AP$ (from ε_{gas} measurements)
CO_2	0·68 c.c.	0·81 c.c.
CH_4	0·091	0·08
C_2H_6	0·14	0·09
C_2H_4	0·40	0·39
N_2O	0·55	0·41 or 0·46 (1)

(1) Czerlinsky, *Z. Physik*, 1934, **88**, 515. The other five are as stated by Watson and Ramaswamy, *Proc. Roy. Soc.*, 1936, **156A**, 144.

Highly accurate dipole moment values are now gradually becoming available from certain studies involving 'micro-waves' (frequencies of the range 20,000–30,000 megacycles/sec.). These are independent of ε measurements. The troublesome extrapolation of polarizations to high temperatures (i.e. to $1/T = 0$, see above) may therefore be avoided by calculating $_OP$ for a temperature at which $_TP$ is also known. By subtraction $_DP$ and thence, from $_DP - _EP$, $_AP$ should be accessible to serve as a check on the indications of the older method. For instance, the moment of HCN using micro-waves is reported as $2\cdot957\pm0\cdot025D$ by Schulman and Townes (*Phys. Rev.*, 1950, **77**, 421), $_OP$ at 300° K. is therefore 174·57–180·58 c.c.; from Smyth and McAlpine (*J. Amer. Chem. Soc.*, 1934, **56**, 1697) $_TP$ at 300° is 183·19 c.c.; $_DP$ is therefore between 2·61 and 8·62 c.c. The R_∞ of HCN is 6·26 c.c. (*Proc. Roy. Soc.*, 1936, **156A**, 144) so that $_AP$ is not likely to exceed 2·4 c.c. and the earlier estimates quoted by Sugden (viz. 6·2 or 8·6 c.c.) are most probably too high.

Atomic polarizations so far cited have been those of fairly small molecules. On looking over their magnitudes, except for an appearance that $_AP$ tends to increase, when similar molecules are compared, with the size of the molecule, there are no other general relationships evident; in particular, there is nothing to justify the conclusion expressed by Sugden (1934) that to take '$_AP$ as 10 per cent of $_EP$ is probably not far from correct' or that $_DP$ may be approximately assumed to be 1·05 times R_D.

The dangers of following such a procedure are demonstrated by the existence of a group of compounds each of which at one time seemed to exhibit a permanent dipole moment despite the possession by its molecular structure of a centre of symmetry, i.e. a property normally leading (see later) to a resultant of zero. The first measurements were made in solution and naturally this fact was initially suspected as a cause of the anomalies. Examples are given in the following table:

Substance	Solvent	Apparent Moment
p-dihalogenobenzenes	C_6H_6	0·2 D
p-benzoquinone	C_6H_6 (1, 3, 4)	0·7
	CCl_4	0·7
p-dinitrobenzene	C_6H_6 (5, 6)	0·32–0·60
1:3:5-trinitrobenzene	C_6H_6 (5, 6)	0·70–1·08
	$C_{10}H_8$	0·78
2:4:6-trinitromesitylene	C_6H_6 (5, 6)	0·79–0·9
Trinitro-1:3:5-triethylbenzene	C_6H_6 (6)	0·8
	CCl_4 (6)	0·8
1:3:5-trihalogeno-2:4:6-trinitro-benzenes	C_6H_6 (7)	0·7
Various diaryl mercury compounds, R_2Hg	Decalin	0·54–1·11
Mercuric chloride	Dioxan (8)	1·29
Mercuric bromide	,,	1·06
Mercuric iodide	,,	0·58
Beryllium acetylacetonate	C_6H_6 (2)	1·1
Beryllium basic acetate	C_6H_6 (2)	1·35

(1) Hassel and Naeshagen (*Z. physikal. Chem.*, 1930, **6B**, 441); (2) Angus and Smith (*Proc. Roy. Soc.*, 1932, **137**, 372); (3) Le Fèvre and Le Fèvre (*J.C.S.*, 1935, 1698); (4) Hammick, Hampson and Jenkins (*Nature*, 1935, **136**, 990); (5) Le Fèvre and Le Fèvre (*J.C.S.*, 1935, 957); (6) Jenkins (*ibid.*, 1936, 862); (7) Lütgert (*Z. physikal. Chem.*, 1932, **14B**, 27); (8) Curran and Wenzke (*J. Amer. Chem. Soc.*, 1935, **57**, 2162).

The apparent moments shown are those computed by treating as orientation polarizations the differences between the observed total polarizations and the molecular refractions—differences which run from *ca.* 9 up to *ca.* 50 c.c. for compounds whose R_D values are mostly 30–60 c.c. Later work by Finn, Hampson and Sutton (*J.C.S.*, 1938, 1254) not only established the case of beryllium acetylacetonate as anomalous but revealed that the related derivatives of Zn, Cu, Al, Fe, Co, Th, and Zr were even more remarkable instances, e.g. the acetylacetonates of Fe^{III}, Th, and Zr had apparent moments of 1·7, 1·8, and 1·7D respectively.

The ultimate resolution of the problem came from an outstanding experimental investigation made by Coop and Sutton (*J.C.S.*, 1938, 1269). The total polarizations of a number of acetylacetonates, of benzoquinone, *p*-dinitrobenzene, &c., were measured in the vapour phase over the widest temperature ranges possible: the $(_TP)_{gas}$ figures so obtained were all near the corresponding values of $(_TP)_{solution}$ and moreover were substantially independent of temperature. The excesses of $_TP$ over $_EP$ were therefore neither genuine orientation polarizations—since these would have varied as $1/T$—nor caused by solvents—since they occurred without them. They were evidently *atomic polarizations*.

Their origins were explained by Sutton as follows: Every relative movement of nuclei which is associated with a change in the dipole moment of a molecule must occur when a field is applied: movements such as alterations in length of polar bonds, of angles between such bonds, and the mutual bending or twisting of polar groups. If, now, the applied field is not static but is *alternating* with a frequency f_0, account must be taken of the tendency for the internuclear movements to take place with natural frequencies f_i, which are dependent on the respective restoring forces F_i, and the effective masses m_i moved. If these restoring forces obey Hooke's law the relation $f_i=(1/2\pi)(F_i/m_i)^{\frac{1}{2}}$ holds. The average degree of deformation depends upon the average amplitude forced by the field upon these vibrators; it will depend upon the field strength through the proportionality factor (or polarizability) γ_A (p. 4); this by classical methods is $e_i^2/12\pi^2 m_i(f_i^2-f_0^2)$. Writing $F_i/4\pi^2f_i^2$ for m_i, we have—since $_AP=4\pi N\gamma_A/3$—

$$_AP_i=4\pi Ne_i^2f_i^2/9F_i(f_i^2-f_0^2),$$

which when $f_0 \to 0$, reduces to $_AP_i = 4\pi Ne_i^2/9F_i$ for an independent one-dimensional oscillator in which an effective mass m_i is carrying an effective charge e_i. The total (or molecular) atomic polarization is therefore the sum of the $_AP_i$ terms for all oscillations accompanied by alterations in dipole moment, i.e. all those having fundamentals 'active' in absorption or emission infra-red spectra. A displacement δl of an effective charge e_i along a bond length l will cause a change of bond moment of $\delta\mu$, i.e. $\delta\mu/\delta l = e_i$, but even if e_i were equal to the full electronic charge (so that $\mu_{\text{equilibrium}} = ca.\ 8\text{--}10D$), the magnitudes of F_i for stretching modes are so great that $_AP_i$ would not exceed 0·5 c.c. In general, $\mu_{\text{equilibrium}}$ is less than $3D$ and accordingly Sutton concluded that the main contributions to $_AP$ come from vibrations involving variations of the angles between bonds, the forces required for such motions being commonly of the order of a tenth of those required to alter bond lengths by comparable amounts. He showed that for changes in the angles between two similar dipoles at a normal angle π, $_AP = 4\pi N\mu_i^2/9V_i$, where V_i is a force constant of bending.

Bending force constants lie around 10^{-11} erg/radian, the value for a given pair of bonds being often markedly sensitive to their molecular situations (see Linnett, *Quarterly Revs.*, 1947, **I**, 73). When available, however, they permit an *a priori* estimate of $_AP$. Thus cyanogen contains two independent oscillators—each C≡N bond relative to the central C—C link—and each of these is two-dimensional, therefore $_AP = 4 \times 4\pi N\mu_i^2/9V_i$; V_i is $2\cdot93 \times 10^{-12}$ erg/radian, and $\mu_{C\equiv N}$ from $2\cdot5\text{--}3D$. With these data $_AP$ is between 7·2 and 10·4 c.c.; the value from experiment is 8·34 c.c. Again for a tetrahedral molecule, e.g. methane, $_AP$ also equals $16\pi N\mu_i^2/9V_i$; since V_i for the CH_2 angle is *ca.* 5×10^{-12} erg/radian and μ_{C-H} about $0\cdot4D$, $_AP_{CH_4}$ follows as 0·11 c.c. (against 0·08 c.c. reported by Watson *et al.*).

With many molecules, however, appropriate bending force constants are as yet unknown. For example, p-benzoquinone has $_DP-_EP=8.2$ c.c.; treating each $C=O$ group as a one-dimensional oscillator, bending in the plane of the ring, and putting $\mu_{CO}=2.5D$, we obtain 1.3×10^{-12} erg/radian for V_i. With the acetylacetonates we may consider each chelate ring to vibrate in a plane perpendicular to its own, and to carry a moment probably between 6 and $9D$, then—if x is the number of chelate rings—$_AP=4\pi Nx\mu_i^2/9V_i=25.5$, 40.2, 55.1 or 72.5 c.c. for the Be, Cr, Fe or Th compounds (for which $x=2$, 3, 3 or 4 respectively), and—if μ_i is say $7.5D$—V_i becomes, in order, 3.7, 3.6, 2.6 or 2.6×10^{-12} erg/radian. Such figures have the magnitudes reasonably to be expected for the deformations concerned.

To summarize: Sutton's theory provides a workable explanation of atomic polarization. It brings together consistently various indications from past experiments. In particular it shows (a) why if several molecules contain essentially the same oscillating systems their $_AP$ values are roughly the same (e.g. compare: cyanogen, fumaronitrile and 1:4-dicyanobenzene for which $_AP=8.3$, 9.8, and 11.9 c.c., or benzoquinone, carbon suboxide and tetramethyl*cyclo*butadione whose atomic polarizations are all 8–10 c.c.), (b) why $_AP$ cannot be generally a constant fraction of $_EP$ (since the former depends on the presence of polar groups while the latter does not), and (c) why $_AP$ can sometimes, with a series of related compounds, show signs of additivity (e.g. with the metallic acetylacetonates, where $_AP$ crudely follows the number of rings attached to the central metal atom).

On present knowledge, therefore, it is difficult to evaluate dipole moments with certainty by the refractivity method. Fortunately the larger is the difference between $_TP$ and $_DP$, the smaller becomes the error in μ

caused by a variation $\partial_D P$ in $_D P$: from the equation $\mu = 0 \cdot 01281 \sqrt{(_T P - _D P)T}$, it can be seen that

$$\partial \mu / \mu = -(\partial_D P / _D P)_D P / 2(_T P - _D P).$$

In some cases the allowance for $_A P$ may be calculated following Sutton, but when this is not possible, it seems better to regard $(R_L)_D$ as an incomplete substitute for $_D P$, and to accept this approximation as an interim one, pending the development of data requisite for the accurate computation of $_A P$. Neither the $1 \cdot 05 R_L$ or 10 per cent $_E P$ 'rules', or empirical equations involving the refraction (e.g. Treiber *et al.*, *Zeit. Naturforsch.*, 1950, **5a**, 208), can be justifiably recommended as alternatives.

DETERMINATION OF DIPOLE MOMENTS FROM MEASUREMENTS ON SOLUTIONS

The methods of measurement reviewed above apply strictly only when mutual interaction of the molecules can be regarded as negligible. For gases at high pressures and with liquids this condition is certainly not fulfilled.

The molecules of a dipolar substance will, depending on their relative orientations, exert forces of attraction and repulsion upon one another; accordingly, it is clear that those configurations in which attraction is greatest will be favoured. Thus there will be a tendency— opposed by thermal motion—for the molecules to *associate* together in groups in which they behave as *one* double or triple molecule rather than two or three molecules separately. The process may proceed much further, giving very large aggregates. The particular mode and degree of *association* into complex molecules is conditioned largely by the shape of the molecular species under consideration and the location and magnitude of the resultant dipole moment in it. Thus, commonly occurring orientations have the dipoles of the component molecules aligned (a) antiparallel, (b) colinearly and reinforcing one another, or (c) and (d) in various other head-to-tail and sideways-on arrangements. These possibilities are indicated in the accompanying diagrams.

It is to be noted that the resultant dipole moment of the group (a) is equal to the moment of a single molecule only, that of the group (b) is three times this, whilst (c) or (d) has actually a zero moment. The effect which such association can have upon the dielectric constant of a liquid is obvious if equation (4) be altered to apply to

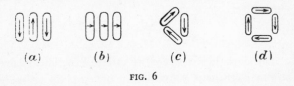

(a) (b) (c) (d)

FIG. 6

a system in which the molecules have aggregated to the units (a), (b), (c), and (d).

The molecular weight must be rewritten for (a), (b), and (c) as $3M$ and for (d) as $4M$, while the moment will be in the four cases: μ, 3μ, o, o, respectively; γ_E and γ_A remain the same. Only for (b) will $\frac{\varepsilon-1}{\varepsilon+2}$ have a larger value than it does for a system of single molecules; therefore, since the majority of molecules do not tend to associate as in (b), it is in most cases true that dipole moment values calculated from dielectric constant, density, refractive index, &c., measurement on pure polar liquids, are far too low.

The Mixture Laws. In a liquid mixture containing W_1 and W_2 parts by weight of two components there are present W_1/M_1 and W_2/M_2 molecules of the two substances respectively. It is convenient to speak of the *molar fraction* of each component; these are given by

$$f_1 = W_1 M_2 / (W_1 M_2 + W_2 M_1)$$

and

$$f_2 = W_2 M_1 / (W_2 M_1 + W_1 M_2).$$

It has been known for many years that the molecular refraction of a liquid mixture is the sum of the refractions of its components, i.e. if these be written R_1 and R_2, the refractive indexes be n_1 and n_2, densities be d_1 and d_2, and if the subscript $_{12}$ denotes the mixture, then

$$R_{12} = \frac{n^2_{12} - 1}{n^2_{12} + 2} \cdot \frac{M_1 f_1 + M_2 f_2}{d_{12}}$$

$$= \frac{n^2_1 - 1}{n^2_1 + 2} \cdot \frac{M_1 f_1}{d_1} + \frac{n^2_2 - 1}{n^2_2 + 2} \cdot \frac{M_2 f_2}{d_2}.$$

The deviations revealed by careful experiment have seldom exceeded 1 per cent.

Attempts to utilize the Clausius-Mosotti formula similarly are usually less satisfactory owing to the effects of molecular association within and between the two components. Where solutions of a polar solute in a non-polar solvent are considered, however, the problem is simpler since the polarization of the latter can be calculated with fair accuracy as $P_1 f_1$ (where P_1 is the total polarization $(\varepsilon_1 - 1)/(\varepsilon_1 + 2) . M_1/d_1$ of the pure solvent, which, containing no orientation term, is not sensibly affected by association); thus $P_2 f_2$ can be evaluated as a difference between the (measured) total polarization of the solution and the (calculated) solvent contribution.

$$P_2 f_2 = \frac{\varepsilon_{12} - 1}{\varepsilon_{12} + 2} \cdot \frac{M_1 f_1 + M_2 f_2}{d_{12}} - P_1 f_1.$$

The apparent polarization of the solute is then obtained by division; experimentally it is found to vary with the concentration f_2, generally increasing as dilution proceeds. In this respect the result recalls the effect which solute association can have in molecular weight determination, when the true molecular weight of the single molecule is obtainable by an extrapolation to infinite dilution. Analogous treatment of polarization

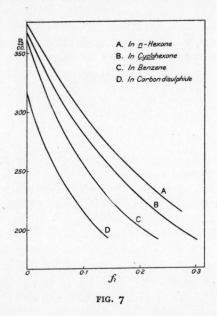

A. In *n*-Hexane
B. In *Cyclohexane*
C. In Benzene
D. In Carbon disulphide

FIG. 7

data lead to a value for the 'polarization at infinite dilution', written as $_\infty P_2$, which should be the value of the polarization of the solute when each molecule is surrounded by the non-polar molecules of the solvent. Fig. 7 shows the change of P_2 for nitro-benzene in four different solvents. In order, $_\infty P_2$, is generally close to the total polarization measured for the solute in the gaseous state, after the two figures have been brought to a common temperature basis. More important, however, is the experimental fact that solutions display the temperature dependence indicated by equation (4), namely, that the polarization at infinite dilution varies linearly with the reciprocal of the absolute temperature. Some examples are shown in Fig. 8.

The horizontal line for hexane shows that its polarization is invariant with temperature—i.e. that $_0P = 0$ and

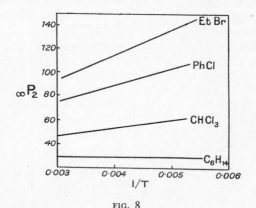

FIG. 8

therefore $\mu = 0$—whilst from the slopes of the curves for the other substances values for B in the equation $P = A + B/T$ can be obtained. The intercepts at $1/T = 0$ give the quantities $(_EP + _AP)$. In general, distortion polarizations provided in this way appear to exceed those shown by corresponding experiments with the solutes as gases (e.g. $_EP + _AP$ from $P_2 \times 1/T$ graphs for ethyl bromide in benzene is apparently 25 c.c. while from those for this material as a vapour the figure is 22 c.c.); such disagreements may have their origins in 'solvent effects' (see later), but, additionally, it is frequently difficult to secure an adequate temperature range for the accurate measurement of $(P_2)_{T_1}$ and $(P_2)_{T_2}$—the maximum being, of course, that between the m.p. and b.p. of the medium.

In conclusion, it is thus possible to calculate a value for the dipole moment of a molecule from data on dilute solutions in non-polar solvents either by (1) the temperature method (requiring observation at a number of temperatures) or (2) the refractivity method, in which $_\infty P_2$ is found for one temperature only, and $(_E P +_A P)$ approximately estimated from the molecular refractions and other sources already discussed.

The degree of justification for working with solutions may be gauged by comparing results so produced with those recorded with the vaporized substances. Unfortunately, such tests were first made with several compounds for which considerable differences between μ_{gas} and $\mu_{dissolved}$ would not now be expected. The following table will illustrate how in some cases agreement can be quite inexact.

TABLE II

Substance	Gas	Dipole Moment from Measurements on Solutions in Benzene		
		(1)*	(2)*	(3)*
Ethyl alcohol	$1 \cdot 70 D$**	$1 \cdot 72 D$	$1 \cdot 74 D$	$1 \cdot 74 D$
Chloroform	$1 \cdot 01$	$1 \cdot 13$	$1 \cdot 21$	—
Thionyl chloride	$1 \cdot 44$	$1 \cdot 54$	$1 \cdot 58$	$1 \cdot 38$
Sulphuryl chloride	$1 \cdot 80$	$1 \cdot 82$	$1 \cdot 86$	$1 \cdot 64$
Diethyl ether	$1 \cdot 17$	$1 \cdot 26$	$1 \cdot 30$	$1 \cdot 15$
Paraldehyde	$1 \cdot 44$	$1 \cdot 98$	$2 \cdot 12$	—
Chlorobenzene	$1 \cdot 73$	$1 \cdot 54$	$1 \cdot 59$	$1 \cdot 61$
Nitrobenzene	$4 \cdot 24$	$3 \cdot 97$	$3 \cdot 97$	$3 \cdot 96 - 3 \cdot 99$

* (1) using true $_D P$ figures; (2) taking $(R_L)_D = _D P$; (3) by temperature method on solutions.

** $D =$ 'Debye units', i.e. 10^{-18} e.s.u.

GENERAL REFERENCES

Debye, *Polar Molecules*, New York, 1929

Smyth, *Dielectric Constant and Chemical Structure*, New York, 1931

Van Vleck, *Theory of Electric and Magnetic Susceptibilities*, Oxford, 1932

CHAPTER II

PRACTICAL METHODS FOR THE
MEASUREMENT OF DIPOLE MOMENTS

FOR the various methods outlined above the following information is required: the total polarization at known temperatures, or the variation of polarization with state, and the molecular refraction, preferably at several wavelengths. The individual observations necessitated, therefore, are the dielectric constant, density, refractive index, and concentration, of the molecular species under examination.

Experimentally, measurements with gaseous substances are more difficult than with liquids; this arises partly from the special technique required, but chiefly

FIG. 9

from the fact that the dielectric constants of gases differ so slightly from unity. The particular details of dielectric constant measurement will be discussed below for the two cases, but certain general observations can be made here.

Ultimately, as the definition shows, the dielectric constant of a material implies a comparison of the capacities of a condenser respectively filled with the substance and empty. Although a number of methods exist by which this can be done, all modern investigators have employed some application of the following elementary electrical facts. A circuit (Fig. 9) consisting of capacity C, inductance L, and resistance R joined in series will be set into electrical oscillation if the condenser is suddenly given a charge and then left to discharge. The current flowing after time t secs. is given approximately by

$$i_t = i_0 e^{-\frac{Rt}{2L}} \sin \frac{t}{\sqrt{LC}}.$$

Clearly, if the total resistance of the circuit could be reduced to zero, the exponential decay factor would become unity and the oscillations continue indefinitely. An approach to this condition is realized in regenerative and transconductance oscillators, which are simply devices by which a negative resistance is introduced into the circuit mentioned. The angular frequency of such oscillations is $1/\sqrt{LC}$, i.e. it depends only upon the dimensions of the inductances and capacities forming the circuit. If, however, an *external* electromagnetic vibration be applied to the LCR circuit above, *induced* oscillations will be set up in it; these will be at maximum strength when the applied frequency satisfies the equation: $f = (1/2\pi)(1/LC)^{\frac{1}{2}}$. The circuit will then be in '*resonance*' with the applied vibration.

If, now, the capacity C is split into a standard condenser C_1 and a condenser C_2, the dielectric of which can be replaced or evacuated, the various capacities which C_2 assumes can be compared by tuning the circuit either to resonance with some constant source of oscillations or, alternatively, to some fixed frequency. These can be effected by adjustment of C_1. Then $C = C_1 + C_2$ and any increase in C_2 must be compensated by an equivalent diminution of C_1, and *vice versa*. The differences between methods are mainly in the devices adopted for matching frequencies or for detecting resonance.

By reason of the small dielectric constants of gases the capacity changes caused by their introduction into an evacuated condenser are small, so that correspondingly fine standard condensers, and frequency or resonance indicators, are necessary.

The 'heterodyne beat' method was the first to be employed in the more modern investigations. In principle it is simple: The experimental cell, C, in conjunction with a calibrated variable condenser, V, and an inductance is placed in one of the tuned circuits of an oscillator, such as that shown in Fig. 10.

Situated a few feet away is a similar oscillator designed to generate radiations at some *constant* frequency close to

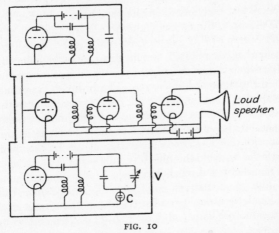

FIG. 10

the first. If a pick-up and amplifier is fed from both circuits the beats between them can be rendered audible in headphones or a loud-speaker; their number per second is the *difference* between the two frequencies. Identity of frequency in the two circuits can be obtained by adjustment of the variable condenser in the first oscillator and will be indicated by silence. This point is not usually sharp; workers have, therefore, often used instead an audible frequency as the reference standard and have fixed this by referring it to some steady note, such as that from an electrically driven tuning-fork.

Zahn (*Physical Rev.*, 1924, **24**, 400) was one of the first to employ this method for dipole moment measurement; the technique has been carried to a considerable degree of refinement in the work of Watson and collaborators (*Proc. Roy. Soc.*, 1934, **143**, 558). Groves (*J.C.S.*, 1935, 1144) later used a cathode-ray tube to display the frequency match-point between the primary oscillators and thus eliminated the trouble of maintaining a constant ancillary standard. Typical circuits may be seen in the papers just mentioned. Others have been published by, for example, Stranathan (*Rev. Sci. Instr.*, 1934, **5**, 334) and Sutton (*J.C.S.*, 1938, 1269, and 1941, 727). All are somewhat complicated, and for this reason the following alternative is now described.

A Recommended Apparatus. The ordinary resonance method as used for liquids (cf. later) is useless since the point of maximum resonance given by the most sensitive indicators is not sharp enough to show the alterations of capacity due to gaseous dielectrics. It can be modified, however, to avoid this difficulty and thus offer advantages of simplicity and reliability.

The gas containing condenser, C_g, is included, with a standard variable condenser, C_p, in the circuit of a Franklin oscillator, A (see Fig. 11). The frequency

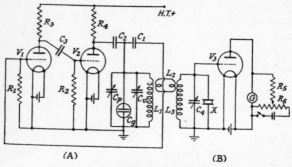

(A)   (B)

FIG. 11

generated in this circuit depends upon a product LC as before; a frequency f_Q is chosen as a reference frequency such that f_Q is the natural frequency of a section of a quartz crystal forming the dielectric of a small condenser, X, in a nearby pick-up circuit, B, the dimensions of which are arranged so that it, in turn, resonates at f_Q when X is not in circuit. Resonance is indicated by deflections in G, a galvanometer in the anode circuit of the valve voltmeter shown on the right-hand side of B. A and B are built on separate steel chassis, C_g, C_v, and C_p being connected to the chassis by short lengths of coaxial

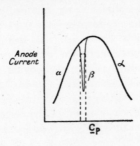

FIG. 12

cable. The operation of the arrangement is simple; with X not in circuit the anode current from valve V_3 will vary with the capacity in C_p (i.e. with the oscillation frequency of circuit A) in some such manner as the curve α of Fig. 12; with X in the circuit, however, a frequency will exist at which the quartz will be set in mechanical resonance. This behaviour arises from the piezo electric properties of quartz; when compressed, a quartz crystal develops electrical poles; conversely, if positive and negative charges are applied at suitable points a change of shape will ensue. If, therefore, an alternating potential be applied, a frequency can be found at which mechanical resonance will occur, the actual critical frequency in a given case depending upon the piece of quartz employed. A complete natural crystal is hexagonal in cross-section and for dielectric purposes the best results are obtained if the slices are cut so that their sides form planes at right angles to that plane which runs between any pair of opposite corners in the parent crystal. The frequency at which such a section will resonate in X is given approximately by $f = 2730/x$, where f is in kilocycles/sec. and x (the thickness) in millimetres. In the present instance resonance is indicated by a very sharp absorption of energy, made evident by the changes of anode current shown in curve β. The width of the resulting 'crevasse' being only of the order $1/5 \ \mu\mu F$ allows A to be tuned to a definite frequency and changes in C_g or C_p of the order $0.0002 \ \mu\mu F$ to be easily detected. Readings are taken ascending and descending the sides of the crevasse and their mean regarded as a reference point. Similar observations are made when air, CO_2, &c., are in the gas condenser, and the results with these standard gases enable the dielectric constant of any other substances to be determined *relatively*, exactly as is described later for liquids.

The Cell C_g. A suitable gas cell may be made from three coaxial rhodium-plated brass cylinders (16 gauge) separated by small rectangular quartz spacers, 12 in all, the inner and outer cylinders (each 10 cm. long and earthed) being connected by a ring fitting tightly between them; a H.T. lead is led out, from the middle cylinder (9 cm. long), through a hole in the ring *via* a glass bush. The assembly is pressed together and sealed into an annular 'Pyrex' glass cylindrical vessel, provided with a gas inlet. The leads are of 26 S.W.G. platinum wire, and penetrate the top of the vessel to the lower ends of mercury-filled glass tubes, into which dip the connections first to a shielded coaxial cable union and thence to the oscillator. The empty capacity should be roughly

$200\ \mu\mu$F. The whole is immersed in an oil or (preferably) a vapour thermostat such as that indicated in Fig. 13. Suitable tubes for admitting the gases and vaporizing

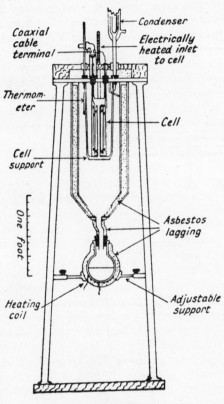

FIG. 13

the substances, leading to a pump and a pressure gauge, &c., need also to be attached to the cell. If carbon dioxide or sulphur dioxide are employed as standard gases,

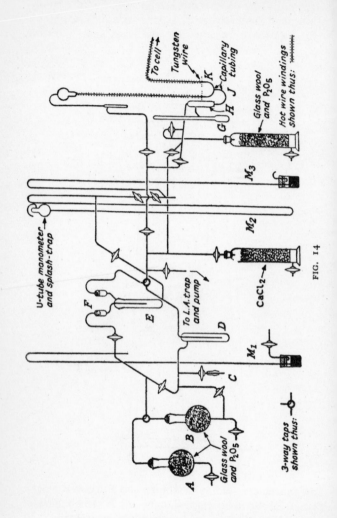

FIG. 14

To cell

Tungsten
wire

Capillary
tubing

K

H J

G

Glass wool
and P₂O₅

Hot wire windings
shown thus:

M₃

M₂

U-tube manometer
and splash-trap

F

E

To L.A. trap and pump

CaCl₂

D

M₁

C

Glass wool
and P₂O₅

A B

3-way taps
shown thus:

The bulbs A and B contain phosphoric oxide dispersed on glass wool, to serve for the preliminary drying of the gases. The connection of the traps (E, D) is such as to permit repeated cyclic distillation of gases. Of these traps, E is removable, and can thus be partly filled with drying agents, distillation over phosphoric oxide having been found the most effective method of drying. The bulbs F, containing plugs of glass wool, serve to prevent phosphoric oxide being carried through the rest of the system when the liquid in the trap bumps while boiling.

The various connections to manometers enable a check to be kept on the pressures in all parts of the apparatus while distillation is in progress—a necessary precaution when icing of the downpipes of the traps occurs, with possible building up of back-pressures during distillation. M_2 is a U-tube manometer for working at positive pressures, and is equipped with a splash-trap.

The system to the right of M_3 is the device used by Groves and Sugden ($J.C.S.$, 1934, 1094; 1939, 1144, 1147) for the vaporization of liquids and their introduction as gases into C_{g}. The CO_2 or SO_2 may be taken from cylinders and redistilled between D and E. Dry air has also been used for calibration (cf. Coop and Sutton, $J.C.S.$, 1938, 1269); its adoption allows Fig. 14 to be simplified somewhat, auxiliary apparatus will therefore be necessary for the preparation, purification, and supply of these. A train for this purpose is shown diagrammatically in Fig. 14.

The Condenser C_p. Earlier workers often placed one of the commercially available precision instruments, having variations upwards from about 50 to 250 or more $\mu\mu$F, in the 'series' position (as is V in Fig. 10). Such an arrangement, however, does not provide a uniform connection between the capacities in C_g and the scale readings on V. It is preferable therefore to link a condenser

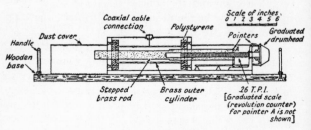

FIG. 15

of smaller range in parallel to the cell (as is C_p in Fig. 11). A satisfactory pattern, easily fabricated with a good lathe, is shown in Fig. 15. It consists of a rod which increases in diameter suddenly at its middle. This 'step' is screwed axially into an insulated brass cylinder (internal diameter 4·7 cm.) forming the non-earthed component and held tightly by grooved rings of polystyrene fixed to the $\frac{1}{2}$-in. steel end-plates. The stepped brass rod (diameters 3·0 and 2·68 cm.) slides through graphite-lubricated bearings on the steel end-plates. The steel screw on which the rod rotates has a pitch of 26 turns per inch and is ground true with the threaded sleeve of the rod. The total capacity of the condenser is *ca.* 30–40 $\mu\mu$F and the variable range 4 $\mu\mu$F traversed by about 100 turns. A pointer moves against a linear scale, indicating numbers of turns, while the rotating head (marked in hundredths) gives fractions of turns.

A condenser built in this manner displays an almost straight-line relation between its capacity and the position of the step; accordingly (ε_x-1) for a dielectric x may be expressed directly in terms of $(\varepsilon-1)$ of a standard gas as $(\varepsilon-1)n_2/n_1$, where n_1 and n_2 are the 'numbers of turns' between the settings of C_p for the centres of the crevasses when C_g is evacuated and filled respectively with the standard or the unknown. Fuller information on the erection and operation of apparatus of the types mentioned may be found in *Trans. Far. Soc.*, 1947, **43**, 374, or *J.C.S.*, 1950, 276 and 290.

Calculation of Results. The total polarization $_TP$ (Ch. I, Equation 5) incorporates the molecular volume (M/d) of a vapour examined. It is not, however, necessary to make special determinations of the density, which may be indirectly measured by the pressure in C_g. If the vapour obeys the gas laws, then

$$_TP=(\varepsilon-1).T.10^5/4{\cdot}810p,$$

where p is the pressure in millimetres of mercury and T the absolute temperature of observation.

Many organic vapours, of course, do not conform to the gas laws; to overcome this the apparent $_TP$ figures can be plotted against the corresponding p's and the curve extrapolated to 'zero pressure'. The value so obtained should be the correct molecular polarization.

Since, however, the variables actually obtained by experiment are p and δC, it is—in the writer's opinion—better to perform the extrapolation to $p=0$ with these (δC is defined in what follows as the difference between drum and scale readings of C_p when C_g is filled to a measured pressure p cm., and the mean of the two 'vacuum' readings taken before and after that particular 'vapour' reading).

For each temperature, the dependence of $\delta C/p$ on p is first inspected graphically. A *curve* at this stage may indicate deviations from ideality of the gas. We assume that δC is not only proportional to the change in dielectric constant (*viz.* $\varepsilon_{\text{gas}} - 1$) but also to the number of molecules present per cubic centimetre, i.e. to the density. For an ideal gas the density is, in turn, proportional to the pressure, and $\delta C = k.p$. For a real gas we must substitute for p (the observed pressure), the 'ideal pressure' p_i that would be exerted if Boyle's Law were fulfilled, i.e. $\delta C = k.p_i = kp/(1 - Ap)$, where A is the compressibility; hence $\delta C/p = k/(1 - Ap)$.

This is a non-linear relation. Accordingly $(\delta C/p)_{p=0}$ should be obtained by evaluating x in the power series: $\delta C = xp + yp^2 + \ldots$, the individual readings for δC and p at each temperature being fitted by least squares *via*

$$x = \frac{\Sigma(p\delta C)\Sigma(p^4) - \Sigma(p^2\delta C)\Sigma(p^3)}{\Sigma(p^2)\Sigma(p^4) - (\Sigma p^3)^2}$$

and

$$y = \frac{\Sigma(p\delta C)\Sigma(p^3) - \Sigma(p^2\delta C)\Sigma(p^2)}{\Sigma(p^2)\Sigma(p^4) - (\Sigma p^3)^2}.$$

The required molecular polarization follows from the relative magnitudes at zero pressure of $\delta C/p$ for the dielectric under examination and that for the standard gas adopted. Since as p approaches 0, $\varepsilon + 2$ likewise approaches 3, so that—remembering that

$$\delta C = (constant) \times (\varepsilon - 1)$$

—the Clausius-Mosotti expression may be written: $_TP = K(\delta C/p)_{p\to 0}(pv)_{p\to 0}$, where v is the volume occupied by one mole of gas; but in the limit $(pv)_{p\to 0} = p_i v_i = V$, the molar volume of a perfect gas at one atmosphere. This is a general relation for all gases, K being a constant throughout. Therefore, putting x' as $(\delta C/p)_{p\to 0}$ for the standard gas, and x as the corresponding quantity for the gas being investigated, $_TP$ for the latter is xP_{standard}/x'.

For P_{standard}, the temperature invariant polarizations of air (4·344 c.c. corresponding to $\varepsilon = 1\cdot000582$ at N.T.P.) or carbon dioxide (7·341 c.c. corresponding to $\varepsilon = 1\cdot000905$ at 25° and 760 mm.) are available. Sulphur dioxide has also been recommended for occasions when larger values are required; its total polarization at a given temperature is $10\cdot91 + 16164/T$ c.c.

Finally, from the various $_TP$ and $1/T°$ figures a 'Debye' equation, $(_TP)_{T°} = A + B/T°$, is fitted, using

$$A = \frac{\Sigma(1/T)\Sigma(P/T) - \Sigma(1/T)^2\Sigma(P)}{[\Sigma(1/T)]^2 - n\Sigma(1/T)^2}$$

and $B = \dfrac{\Sigma(1/T)\Sigma(P) - n\Sigma(P/T)}{[\Sigma(1/T)]^2 - n\Sigma(1/T)^2}$, where n is the number of determinations. The dipole moment emerges as $\mu = 0\cdot01281 B^{\frac{1}{2}} . 10^{-18}$ e.s.u.

DIPOLE MOMENT MEASUREMENTS IN SOLUTION

Solvents. Those most commonly employed are benzene and carbon tetrachloride, less frequently dioxan, carbon disulphide, hexane, and other non-polar liquids. They should be pure, and especially dry. Benzene of the commercial 'A.R.' grade may be allowed to stand over fresh sodium wire for a few days and then partially frozen. The solid residue obtained by decantation is usually satisfactory after remelting in contact with clean sodium. Carbon tetrachloride must not be treated with sodium. The purest commercial preparation should be washed successively with concentrated sulphuric acid, water, 2N-sodium hydroxide, and water; drying can be accomplished with anhydrous potassium carbonate or sodium sulphate. After refractionation it can be stored over stick potash. Directions applicable to other solvents may be found in Weissberger and Proskauer's *Organic Solvents* (Oxford, 1935).

Procedure and Densities. A series of solutions of graded concentrations of the compound to be examined are made up by weight, and their densities and dielectric constants determined relatively to the pure solvent at some known temperature. For the former measurements the Perkin modification of Sprengel's pyknometer gives better results than the usual Ostwald-Sprengel type, which cannot be wiped so easily prior to weighing. If they are made of ca. 10 c.c. capacity and provided with capillary side arms the final densities can be accurate to 0·00001. For calibration purposes the following equations may be useful:

$$C_6H_6:—d_t = 0·87378 + 10668 . 10^{-7}(25 - t)$$
$$CCl_4:—d_t = 1·63372 - 199 . 10^{-5}t + 5 . 10^{-7}t^2$$
$$(t \text{ in } ° C.)$$

Dielectric Constants. For these measurements there are a number of apparatus mentioned in the literature. The following arrangement has worked satisfactorily for several years (see *Trans. Far. Soc.*, 1947, **43**, 374, for details). Briefly, a circuit, B, containing the replaceable and standard variable capacities (C_x and C_2 respectively), is tuned to resonance with a constant-frequency generator, A. The latter is stabilized by a quartz crystal, Q, in connection between the grid and filament of the valve V_1. When C_1 is varied a combination of L_1C_1 will ultimately be reached such that the natural frequency of the anode circuit is equal to that of the quartz. The latter will then enter into mechanical resonance and cause a marked drop in the current registered in the milli-ammeter, M. The circuit A is now oscillating at a frequency determined by the physical dimensions and cut of the quartz slice (cf. previous section), and for the present purposes it can be considered a constant-frequency generator. The operation of B is as follows:

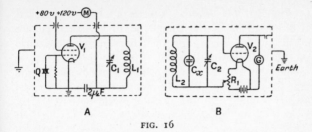

FIG. 16

maximum resonance is found by obtaining the maximum deflection in the galvanometer, G. For every filling of the experimental cell, C_x, a certain setting of the standard variable condenser, C_2, will be required such that $(C_x+C_2)L_2=C_1L_1$. Evaluation of a dielectric constant is then possible as follows: if the capacity required in C_2 with air in the cell is C_A, and with the pure solvent (dielectric constant ε) in C_x is C_B, then the 'zero capacity, i.e. the capacity which would be required with the leads but without the condenser, is given by

$$C_0=(C_A\varepsilon-C_B)/(\varepsilon-1)$$

and if C_s is the capacity required in C_2 for resonance with a solution in C_x, the dielectric constant of the latter is $\varepsilon_s=(C_0-C_s)/(C_0-C_A)$.

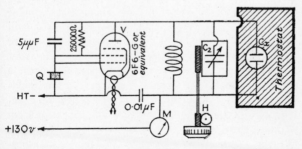

FIG. 17

An alternative apparatus, which is easy to construct, can be based on the left-hand unit of Fig. 16. As an example a simple circuit is shown in Fig. 17. Current supplies may be drawn from the mains through a constant-voltage transformer followed by a conventional radio power-pack (preferably one providing stabilized H.T. by the addition of VR tubes). Its operation utilizes the rapid change in reading seen on M as the anode circuit of V is tuned across the natural frequency

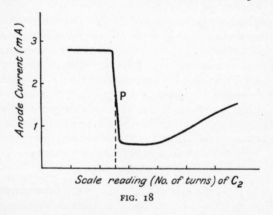

FIG. 18

of the quartz crystal Q (see Fig. 18). The dielectric under examination is placed in C_x, which is connected in parallel to the variable standard C_2. The latter is adjusted until M indicates a point such as P (Fig. 18). Observations are repeated with air and the pure solvent in C_x. Results are calculated as before.

The condenser C_2 is an approximately 50–250 $\mu\mu$F variable semicircular plate instrument (e.g. Sullivan's second grade) fitted with a worm-geared extension handle terminating in a graduated drumhead (*ca.* 4 in. diam.) and revolution counter (H). The capacity of such a condenser is usually proportional to the setting of the moving vanes over the greater part of the scale, and its use should be restricted to within this limit. Readings may be taken in units of 'turns of the rotating head' (H). These can easily be determined with a 0–10 milliamp. meter for M to less than $1/200$ of a turn, the available part of the scale being covered in 35–40 turns. The condenser C_x (see below) should be completely immersible in the thermostat and have extension tubes to enable it to be filled and emptied by air pressure or suction without any alteration of its position. The components are conveniently assembled on and below a metal chassis from which a shielded co-axial cable connection runs to C_x.

Quartz sections of defined frequency response and mounted in sealed holders ready for installation as oscillators or resonators are available commercially.

The Experimental Cell. A satisfactory design for the experimental cell, C_x, is difficult to achieve, and many disagreements among recorded dielectric constants are to be attributed to this point. Theoretically, the condenser should afford direct proportionality between dielectric constant and measured capacity; in practice, such an ideal is never reached because the dielectric medium cannot fill the whole space between the conducting plates. Leads have to pass out to the measuring apparatus and mechanical supports are necessary to fix the conductors in rigid positions relative to each other and to neighbouring bodies. An elementary tube of force in an actual condenser, in passing from one plate to the other, may include a solid dielectric as well as the medium under examination. The total contribution to the capacity of the system by this tube of force will be $(1/C_m + 1/C_s)^{-1}$ (where C_m and C_s are the capacities due to medium and solid elements, respectively). The total capacity between the conductors will, therefore, be $\Sigma[(1/C_m + 1/C_s)^{-1}]$, the summation being performed over all the tubes of force. On the introduction of a fluid of dielectric constant ε the capacity becomes

$$\Sigma[(1/\varepsilon C_m + 1/C_s)^{-1}] = C_T.$$

It is obvious that if there were no C_s, then

$$C_T = \varepsilon \times (\text{a constant}),$$

and the condenser would be an absolute one. However,

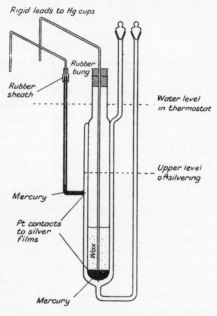

Rigid leads to Hg cups

Rubber bung

Rubber sheath

Water level in thermostat

Upper level of silvering

Mercury

Pt contacts to silver films

Wax

Mercury

FIG. 19

if *either* C_m or C_s vanishes for each individual term of the summation, then $C_T = \varepsilon \Sigma C_m + \Sigma C_s$, i.e. a linear relation obtains between ε and C_T. This condition is realized *if each tube of force passes through only one medium*; it is closely approached in the form of condenser proposed by Sayce and Briscoe. This, with slight modifications, is shown in section in Fig. 19 and consists essentially of two concentric glass tubes fused into a unit at one end. Outlet and inlet tubes are provided which, with the aid of ground-glass auxiliary tubes, enable the condenser to be filled and emptied by suction. The outer surface of the inner tube and the inner surface of the outer are silvered very heavily up to approximately two-thirds of the length. Connection is made to the plates by means of platinum foil fused to the respective surfaces and connected to platinum wires which pass into the interior of the inner tube and into a side tube sealed to the outer tube, respectively. The platinum wire in the inner tube is covered with mercury into which dips a rigid rod which passes axially up the condenser and which is held in place by allowing a thick layer of melted paraffin-wax to solidify above the mercury. The other end of the rod is bent twice at right angles and fits into a mercury cup in an ebonite block attached to the top of the thermostat in which the condenser is immersed. The lead from the outer plate is also rigid and drops similarly into another mercury cup. Two further wires run from the Hg cups to a coaxial cable union mounted as closely as possible. A bridge holds the condenser in the thermostat in a uniform manner. The thermostat water is earthed and care is taken to keep the liquid level constant.

After silvering the appropriate surfaces, the inside is washed several times with pure alcohol followed by benzene, after which dry air is drawn through for some time. The cell is then ready for the determination of C_A (see above). Experience has shown that the vessel should not be left dried out for long periods, otherwise changes in C_0 are liable to occur. After use the silvered portions may be covered with dry benzene.

The creation of thick, strongly adherent silver films can, in practice, be somewhat troublesome. The following directions (from *J.C.S.*, 1933, 770) are recommended.

To AgNO₃ (6 g.) in H₂O (100 c.c.) aqueous NH₃ is added until the precipitate redissolves; 3 per cent NaOH solution (70 c.c.) and more ammonia are added until the solution is just clear. It is diluted to 500 c.c. Glucose (8 g.) in water (150 c.c.) containing nitric acid ($\frac{1}{2}$ c.c.), is boiled for 2 minutes, cooled, and alcohol (150 c.c.) added. The cell is cleaned with a hot mixture of chromic and nitric acids, washed well with distilled water and finally with alcohol. The silver solution (10 parts) is mixed with the glucose solution (1 part) and poured into the condenser through the longer inlet. After $\frac{1}{2}$ hour a dense film is formed.

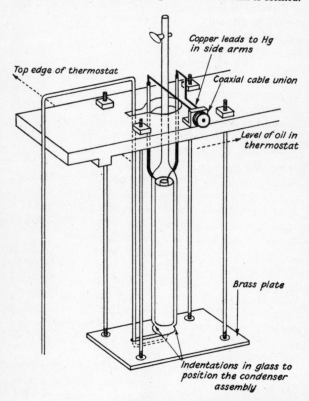

FIG. 20

Three such treatments are sufficient; the vessel is then rinsed with water, &c., as described above. (See also *J. Sci. Instr.*, 1938, **15**, 206.)

To avoid the disturbances caused by the removal of the cell for replating, an assembly of two brass cylinders separated by small pyrex rod spacers may be adopted for routine work. Leads are spot-welded on to the tubes between which, by *slight* distortion in a vice, the pieces of pyrex can then be pressed. The resulting unit is sealed into a pyrex envelope and the whole mounted on a hard-wood bridge (see Fig. 20) spanning the thermostat. Oil, having a lower ε than water, must be used as the bath liquid.

It is convenient to possess a number of cells of different capacities, so that solvents within an ε range of 1·8 to 5 can be employed in the same circuit. The dimensions necessary—knowing the capacity (in $\mu\mu F$) desired—are given nearly enough by $0 \cdot 2416 l / \log_{10}(r_1/r_2)$ where l = length of silvered portion, r_1 = inner radius of outer tube, and r_2 = outer radius of inner tube (l, r_1, r_2 in cm.).

For standardization purified benzene forms the most suitable of the available non-polar solvents. Its dielectric constant at 25° is 2·2725, and at other temperatures is given by the expression: $\varepsilon_t = \varepsilon_{15} + (\delta\varepsilon/\delta t)(t-15)$, in which $\varepsilon_{15} = 2 \cdot 292_{5 \pm 5}$ and $\delta\varepsilon/\delta t = -0 \cdot 0019_{8 \pm 3}$ (cf. Hartshorn and Oliver, *Proc. Roy. Soc.*, 1928, **123A**, 664). For carbon tetrachloride, ε_{25} and $\delta\varepsilon/\delta t$ are 2·2267 and $-0 \cdot 00187$ respectively (Davies, *Phil. Mag.*, 1936, **21**, 1). Data for some other liquids are tabulated in *Trans. Far. Soc.*, 1938, **34**, 1127.

Refractive Indices. The determination of molecular refraction requires no special comment. If a Pulfrich refractometer with a divided cell is used, the differences of refractive index between solvent and solutions can be read with a high accuracy on the graduated drumhead of the micrometer screw by which fine adjustments of the disc holding the telescope are usually made (10 drum divisions≡1 minute).

In many instances negligible error in a final moment, if this is computed by the refractivity method, is caused by *calculating* R_D from the appropriate atomic or bond refractions. Additivity is commonly more satisfactory with the latter (Denbigh, *Trans. Far. Soc.*, 1940, **36**, 926); suitable values are the following (extracted from a list by Vogel, *Chemistry and Industry*, 1950, 358):

Bond	R_D	Bond	R_D
C—H	1·676	C=S	11·91
C—C	1·296	C—N	1·57
C—C (*cyclo*propane)	1·50	C=N	3·75
C—C (,, butane)	1·38	C≡N	4·82
C—C (,, pentane)	1·26	O—H (alcohols)	1·66
C—C (,, hexane)	1·27	O—H (acids)	1·80
C=C	4·17	S—H	4·80
C≡C (terminal)	5·87	S—S	8·11
C_{Ar}—C_{Ar}	2·69	S—O	4·94
C—F	1·45	S→O	−0·20
C—Cl	6·51	N—H	1·76
C—Br	9·39	N—O	2·43
C—I	14·61	N→O	1·78
C—O (ethers)	1·54	N=O	4·00
C=O	3·32	N—N	1·99
C=O (Me ketones)	3·49	N=N	4·12
C—S	4·61		

The above figures display constitutive influences. For the present purposes this is of little consequence in cases where the R_D sought can be estimated from an experimentally measured datum as a starting-point, e.g. $C_6H_5 . NH_2$ has $R_D = 30·58$ c.c., which, minus 1·76 for N—H and plus three times 1·676 for 3(C—H) together with 1·57 for C—N becomes 35·4 (observed for *o*-toluidine, 35·3 c.c.).

Calculation of Results. From the above concentration, ε, and d data the apparent polarizations of the solute in the various solutions can be obtained by application of the mixture relationships set out previously; they will in most cases vary with composition and must be extrapolated to zero-concentration. This can be done graphically or by calculation. The former method is obvious (see Fig. 7, p. 29).

Arithmetical labour can be lightened by using *specific* polarizations, $p = (\varepsilon - 1)/(\varepsilon + 2)d$, in place of molar polarizations; the specific polarization, p_{12}, of a mixture is then: $p_{12} = (1 - w_2)p_1 + w_2p_2$, whence

$$P_2 = M_2p_2 = M_2[p_1 + (p_{12} - p_1)/w_2],$$

in which the suffixes 1 and 2 refer to solvent and solute, respectively, and w_2 is the *weight* fraction (i.e. weight of solute divided by weight of solution) of solute of molecular weight M_2. Similar formulae can be written for refraction. Where the mixture laws are obeyed, a plot of $(p_{12} - p_1)/w_2$ against w_2 is a straight line, so that at infinite dilution, $_\infty p_2 = p_1 + \partial p_{12}/\partial w_2$. To avoid giving undue weight to the experimentally less accurate observations with the weaker solutions, $\partial p_{12}/\partial w_2$ may be evaluated as the quotient $\Sigma(p_{12} - p_1)/\Sigma(w_2)$.

Hedestrand (*Z. physikal. Chem.*, 1929, **B2**, 428) has shown that $_\infty P_2$ might be accessible from the dielectric constant and density of a single solution if the dependence on concentration of each of these properties is known. For instance, when both ε_{12} and d_{12} have *rectilinear* relationships with f_2, then $\varepsilon_{12} = \varepsilon_1(1 + \alpha f_2)$ and $d_{12} = d_1(1 + \beta f_2)$, f_2 being the molar fraction of the solute; these quantities may be substituted for ε_{12} and d_{12} in the equation (p. 28) for the molecular polarization of a mixture. Then at the limit when $f_2 \rightarrow 0$, $P_2 = _\infty P_2$, $\varepsilon_{12} = \varepsilon_1$, $d_{12} = d_1$, and $f_1 = 1$, $_\infty P_2 = A(M_2 - B\beta d_1) + C\alpha\varepsilon_1$, where $A = (\varepsilon_1 - 1)/(\varepsilon_1 + 2)d_1$, $B = M_1/d_1$, and

$$C = 3M_1/d_1(\varepsilon_1 + 2)^2.$$

Specific polarizations and weight fractions may be used analogously, the *specific* polarization of a solute at infinite dilution being $_\infty p_2 = p_1(1 - \beta) + C\alpha\varepsilon_1$, where $p_1 = (\varepsilon_1 - 1)/(\varepsilon_1 + 2)d_1$, $C = 3/d_1(\varepsilon_1 + 2)^2$, and the coefficients α and β refer to the dielectric constants and densities of the solutions examined, the equations $\varepsilon_{12} = \varepsilon_1(1 + \alpha w_2)$ and $d_{12} = d_1(1 + \beta w_2)$ being assumed as applicable. For benzene of d_4^{25} 0·87378 and ε^{25} 2·2725, $p_1 = 0$·34086 c.c. and $C = 0$·18809. Details and examples are recorded in a paper by Le Fèvre and Vine (*J.C.S.*, 1937, 1805).

Instances occur in which the complete representation of ε_{12} and d_{12} needs the addition of a term containing the square of the concentration, e.g. $d_{12} = d_1(1 + \beta w_2 + \delta w_2^2)$; they are revealed in practice by drifts in the apparent magnitudes of $\alpha\varepsilon_1$ and βd_1 when these are extracted for the individual solutions of a set as $(\varepsilon_{12} - \varepsilon_1)/w_2$ or $(d_{12} - d_1)/w_2$. Usually, however, such $(\alpha\varepsilon_1)_{w_2}$ and $(\beta d_1)_{w_2}$ are themselves linear with w_2 and may either be represented graphically against w_2 or fitted to equations of the type $(\alpha\varepsilon_1)_{w_2}$ or $(\beta d_1)_{w_2} = A + Bw_2$. The two constants independent of w_2 are the values of $\alpha\varepsilon_1$ or βd_1 at $w_2 = 0$ and it is these which should be used for computing $_\infty p_2$. Alternatively, calculations may be made directly on the measured differences, $\delta\varepsilon$ or δd, between ε_{12} and ε_1 or d_{12} and d_1 (rather than on the quotients $\delta\varepsilon/w_2$ or $\delta d/w_2$), by putting $(\delta\varepsilon)_{w_2}$ or $(\delta d)_{w_2}$, as appropriate, equal to $Aw_2 + Bw_2^2$, emphasis being in this way shifted towards the higher concentrations where experimental precision is likely to be greater. Were the observational data free from errors, results by both methods would, of course, be the same. The formulae on pp. 44 and 45 can be adapted for these operations.

Halverstadt and Kumler (*J. Amer. Chem. Soc.*, 1942, **64**, 2988) have claimed advantages for the use of specific volumes $(v = 1/d)$ rather than densities. If $b = (v_{12} - v_1)/w_2$ and $a = (\varepsilon_{12} - \varepsilon_1)/w_2$ then

$$_\infty p_2 = (v_1 + b)(\varepsilon_1 - 1)/(\varepsilon_1 + 2) + 3av_1/(\varepsilon_1 + 2)^2.$$

Comparison of this relation with that of Le Fèvre and Vine may be made by noting that, from the definitions of a and b, $a=\alpha\varepsilon_1$ while $b=-\beta/d_{12}$. The H.K. equation therefore becomes, in L.V. nomenclature,

$$_\infty P_2 = p_1(1-\beta d_1/d_{12})+C\alpha\varepsilon_1.$$

Since d_1/d_{12} is unity at infinite dilution, the L.V. or the H.K. routes should, for a given set of data, yield the same $_\infty p_2$.

Halverstadt and Kumler also raise the question of the correct ε_1 for employment in this kind of extrapolation. They think that ε_1 as determined for the pure solvent is unsuitable for incorporation with a range of solutions, and that in its place one should adopt the ε indicated by a curve of ε_{12} *versus* w_2, drawn from the solutions *only*, for the point $w_2=0$. In the writer's opinion this is unnecessary; however, the matter is still under discussion; the following authors refer to it: Cleverdon and Smith (*Trans. Far. Soc.*, 1949, **45**, 109), Le Fèvre (*ibid.*, 1950, **46**, 1), Everard, Hill, and Sutton (*ibid.*, 1950, **46**, 417), and Everard and Sutton (*J.C.S.*, 1951, 16).

The methods so far described are those designed to produce $_\infty P_2$, which often has an interest of its own for investigators; the moment of the solute has therefore to be computed as a second step. Nevertheless, sometimes an estimate of μ_{solute} may be the sole objective; when not required with the highest accuracy this—*via* the corresponding orientation polarization—can be directly produced from ε_{12} and n_{12}^2 measurements on a series of solutions by adopting one of the following procedures: (a) $(\varepsilon_{12}-n_{12}^2)$ is plotted against c_2 (c_2 is the concentration of solute in moles per c.c.). The initial slope gives approximately the value of $_\infty(_0P_2)(\varepsilon_1+2)(n_1^2+2)/3$, hence

$$_\infty(_0P_2)=\frac{3\,\lim_{(c_2=0)}\partial(\varepsilon_{12}-n_{12}^2)/\partial C_2}{(\varepsilon_1+2)(n_1^2+2)}.$$

(b) If, instead of c_2, weight fractions w_2 are used, then—letting v_1 be the specific volume of the solvent,

$$_\infty(_0P_2)=\frac{3M_2v_1.\lim_{(w_2=0)}\partial(\varepsilon_{12}-n_{12}^2)/\partial w_2}{(\varepsilon_1+2)(n_1^2+2)}.$$

(c) Alternatively, if the limiting values at infinite dilution of $\partial\varepsilon_{12}/\partial w_2$ and $\partial n_{12}^2/\partial w_2$ as ascertained by experiment are $\alpha\varepsilon_1$ and vn_1^2 respectively, then

$$_\infty(_0P_2)=3M_2v_1[\alpha\varepsilon_1/(\varepsilon_1+2)^2-vn_1^2/(n_1^2+2)^2].$$

(See—for a—Guggenheim, *Trans. Far. Soc.*, 1949, **45**, 714, and—for b and c—Smith, *ibid.*, 1950, **46**, 394.)

It will be noted that the densities of the solutions are not involved. The error introduced by this simplification can be assessed by subtracting from, for example, the Halverstadt-Kumler equation for $_\infty P_2$ a corresponding equation—viz.

$$R_2=M_2[(v_1+b)(n_1^2-1)/(n_1^2+2)+3v_1vn_1^2/(n_1^2+2)^2]$$

—for the molecular refraction, whereupon the full $(_{\infty 0}P_2)$ is seen to exceed that from (c) above by the extra term $3M_2(v_1+b)(\varepsilon_1-n_1^2)/(\varepsilon_1+2)(n_1^2+2)$. This is negligible when ε_1 and n_1^2 are nearly equal and M_2 not too large. The three 'short-cuts' shown may therefore be fairly safely used with a solvent such as benzene $(\varepsilon_1-n_1^2=ca.\ 0\cdot03)$ but much less so with, say, dioxan $(\varepsilon_1-n_1^2=ca.\ 0\cdot19)$. Obviously, too, they should be avoided if b is large or μ is small (so that $\alpha\varepsilon_1$ approaches vn_1^2 in magnitude).

Significance of Observational Errors. Fundamentally, all the foregoing methods originate from the assumption that polarizations are additive, i.e. that $P_{12}=P_1f_1+P_2f_2$ (or $P_1w_1+P_2w_2$). Accordingly the accuracy with which P_2 can be measured clearly depends upon the concentration of the solution, for as f_2 diminishes, so does the quantity P_2f_2, and errors in P_2 may, therefore, become considerable. The question can be approached as follows:

From the 'mixture' equation given on p. 28 we have

$$(\varepsilon_{12}-1)[M_2 f_2+M_1(1-f_2)]/(\varepsilon_{12}+2)d_{12}=P_2 f_2+P_1(1-f_2).$$

Partial differentiation with respect to ε_{12} gives

$$\partial P_2/P_2=[3\varepsilon_{12}/(\varepsilon_{12}^2+\varepsilon_{12}-2)](P_{12}/P_2).(1/f_2).(\partial\varepsilon_{12}/\varepsilon_{12}).$$

From this, it is seen that an inaccuracy $\partial\varepsilon_{12}/\varepsilon_{12}$ in the relative determination of the dielectric constant will cause a corresponding error $\partial P_2/P_2$ in the molecular polarization of the solute.

Similarly the error due to the inaccuracy $\partial d_{12}/d_{12}$ can be expressed as

$$\partial P_2/P_2= -(P_{12}/P_2).(1/f_2).(\partial d_{12}/d_{12}),$$

i.e. by an equation differing from that involving the dielectric constant in lacking the factor $3\varepsilon_{12}/(\varepsilon_{12}^2+\varepsilon_{12}-2)$. This, for the usual solvents, is nearly unity. *Hence dielectric constants and densities should normally be measured with the same precision.*

The error which an inaccuracy $\partial P_2/P_2$ can cause in the dipole moment is found by differentiating the equation $\mu=0.01281[(P_2-{}_D P)T]^{\frac{1}{2}}$ with respect to P_2:

$$\partial\mu/\mu=(\partial P_2/P_2)P_2/2(P_2-{}_D P)$$

The larger is the moment under measurement the nearer will $P_2/(P_2-{}_D P)$ be to one and therefore the more will the error in the dipole moment tend to follow $\partial P_2/2P_2$. The effect of an incorrectness in ${}_D P$ has been mentioned on p 26.

OTHER METHODS OF DIPOLE MOMENT MEASUREMENT

The dielectric constant methods outlined previously are the best known and most convenient means at present available for dipole moment measurement. Certain others which have from time to time been devised will now be noted briefly.

(1) *The 'Molecular Beam' Method.* This has proved of

value in the estimation of the moments of several compounds of low volatility and solubility (e.g. the alkali halides); it is an adaptation of the Stern-Gerlach determination of the magnetic moments of atoms. The substance is heated to such a temperature that it acquires a perceptible vapour pressure and a dilute stream of molecules allowed to pass, with a velocity set by the temperature, through a pair of narrow slits into a high vacuum. Here the thin ribbon so produced traverses a highly inhomogeneous electric field and is finally received on a brass plate cooled with liquid air. In the absence of an electric field the molecules leave a vertical line on the target plate. With the field on, the trace shifts as a whole because the molecules become slightly dipolar by induction; if, however, the molecules are permanently polar, they will tend to move towards the stronger part of the field to a degree depending on the inclinations of their dipoles to the field. Thus with a polar substance the trace will be broadened in proportion to the dipole moments. Experimentally this method is difficult—cf. Fraser, *Molecular Beams*, Methuen, 1937, Ch. IV—and it has not yet yielded results of a highly quantitative character. Nevertheless, it has considerable promise, not least because by it the dipole moment is measured *directly* at a given temperature (application to problems of intramolecular rotation, &c.) within a temperature range which is in most cases much greater than that available to the dielectric constant method.

(2) *Electrostriction*. When a gas is subjected to an electric field a contraction occurs. If Δv is the volume decrease at constant pressure caused by the application of a field of intensity E and v_0 is the volume in the absence of a field, then

$$|\Delta v / v_0| = E^2(\alpha + \mu^2/3kT)/2kT.$$

In this expression α can be obtained approximately from the molecular refraction. However, owing to the small-ness of the volume changes observed—about 10^{-4} c.c.—the method has so far only given values of dipole moments which are of the same order of magnitude as those obtained from the dielectric constants. For instance, Frivold (*Physikal. Z.*, 1921, **22**, 603) reported the moment of sulphur dioxide *via* electrostriction as $1\cdot74-1\cdot90D$; Kliefoth (*Z. Physik.*, 1926, **39**, 402) later lowered the figure to $1\cdot70D$. From ε_{gas} measurements the moment is $1\cdot62D$ (*J.C.S.*, 1950, 276).

(3) *Dependence of ε on Field Strength.* Herweg has shown that if the dielectric constant of a polar liquid is determined under a potential gradient of 25,000 or more volts/cm. the value obtained is $\Delta\varepsilon$ different from that ordinarily known for low field strengths. Quantitatively, $\Delta\varepsilon = 4\pi n E^2\mu^4/15k^3T^3(1-\theta)^4$, where n is the number of molecules per c.c., E is the field in absolute volts/cm., and θ is the volume polarization, $(\varepsilon-1)/(\varepsilon+2)$. As an example: at 18° diethyl ether had $\Delta\varepsilon = 31\cdot39.10^{-6}$ under $88\cdot66$ abs.v./cm., whence $\mu = 1\cdot24D$, in fair agreement with $1\cdot17D$ obtained from the polarization-temperature relationship for ether vapour (see Herweg and Pötzsch, *Z. Physik.*, 1922, **8**, 1, and Kautzsch, *Physikal. Z.*, 1928, **29**, 105). The last author recommends the extrapolation of μ against E^2 to $E=0$. In this way he finds for ether and chloroform moments of $1\cdot20$ and $1\cdot01D$ respectively.

(4) *Thermal Effects in Dielectrics.* According to the theory of Debye (*Trans. Far. Soc.*, 1934, **30**, 689; *Physikal. Z.*, 1934, **35**, 101) the absorption of energy by a dielectric is—within certain limitations—proportional to the square of the moment. An easy and rapid method, based on this fact, for the approximate determination of electric moments, would therefore consist in measuring the heating effect of such absorption. An alternating field of a high frequency should be applied between two plates of a simple condenser immersed in the liquid under

examination. If the latter is contained in the bulb of a dilatometer the expansion due to the heating can be readily observed. Experiments have shown that non-polar as well as polar liquids commonly show such expansion; for this reason measurements must be made relatively. The method is applicable to solutions. For further details, see Martin (*Physikal. Z.*, 1936, **37**, 665), Holzmüller (*ibid.*, 1937, **38**, 574), &c.

(5) *Microwave Absorption by Liquids.* The return to random order of an assemblage of polar molecules in a liquid dielectric from which an impressed electric field is suddenly withdrawn is not instantaneous. Molecular inertia and environmental viscous forces have to be overcome (hence the source of the heat evolved in method 4 above). The process may be characterized, in a given case, by a 'relaxation time' τ sec. Using assumptions involving Stoke's law and the shapes of molecules, τ can be roughly estimated as $4\pi\eta r^3/kT$, where η is the macroscopic viscosity (in poises) and r is the molecular radius (in centimetres). Since η for many organic liquids is around 0·01 poise and r is usually a few A units (10^{-8} cm.), τ is seen to have the order 10^{-10} or 10^{-11} sec.

It is qualitatively obvious that in a liquid dielectric submitted to an alternating field there will be a difference in phase between field intensity and polarization by orientation. Supposing this field to have an angular frequency ω, i.e. to make ω reversals in 2π sec., then clearly the measured total polarization must be some function of ω. Debye has shown that the required relation is a modification of equation (4) on p. 10, namely,

$$(\varepsilon-1)M/(\varepsilon+2)d=(4\pi N/3)[\gamma_E+\gamma_A+\mu^2/(1+iw\tau)3kT]$$

(cf. Debye, *Polar Molecules*, Ch. V, for a full discussion on these topics). The phase lag mentioned is expressed as a 'loss angle' δ for the dielectric; $\tan \delta$ is the 'power factor'; both these vary with ω. Theory indicates that for solutions in, for example, benzene

$$\tan \delta = [(\varepsilon+2)^2 4\pi^2 \mu^2 cN/27\varepsilon kT][\omega\tau/(1+\omega^2\tau^2)],$$

where ε is the dielectric constant of the solution, μ is the dipole moment of the solute molecule whose concentration is c moles per c.c., τ is the relaxation time of the solute, and where N, k and T are, in order, Avogadro's number, Boltzmann's constant and absolute temperature. The smaller quantity in square brackets has a maximum when $\omega\tau=1$, i.e. when the applied field has an angular frequency of about 10^{10} radians/sec., corresponding approximately to 1600 megacycles/sec.—a frequency in the 'microwave' region.

By use of modern transmission line or wave-guide techniques developed for such radiation, accurate measurements may be made of the small power factors shown by dilute solutions of polar solutes in non-polar solvents (cf. *Far. Soc. Discussion* on 'Dielectrics', Section D). Observation of $\tan \delta$ for two frequencies allows in principle the extraction of both μ and τ from the above equation. Samples of the results thus obtained by two sets of workers (Whiffen and Thompson, and Cripwell and Sutherland, *Dielectrics*, pp. 114 and 149) are tabulated:

Substance	τ*	$\mu(D)$	Substance	τ*	$\mu(D)$
Acetone	3·2, 3·4	2·58, 2·6	Toluene	7·3, 7·6	0·30, 0·3
Benzophenone	18, 22	2·81, 2·88	Chlorobenzene	7·5, 10·9	1·51, 1·52
Cyclohexanone	6·5, 10·5	2·90, 3·02	Bromobenzene	10	1·51
Nitromethane	3·9, 4·4	2·81, 2·87	Nitrobenzene	11·5, 13·0	3·75, 3·88
Methyl acetate	3·1, 3·7	1·58, 1·65	Ethyl benzoate	12, 17·6	1·85, 2·02

* In units of 10^{-12} sec.

The moments deduced in this way agree fairly well with values previously found for these solutes by the older methods already described.

Whiffen and Thompson studied the variation of $\tan \delta$ with temperature at a constant ω. Substantially the μ and

τ figures so produced were the same as from the tan $\delta - \omega$ relation:

Substance	From Two Frequencies		From Two Temperatures	
	$\tau \times 10^{12}$	$\mu(D)$	$\tau \times 10^{12}$	$\mu(D)$
Toluene (pure liquid)	7·3	0·30	7·7	0·32
p-Cymene ,,	10·0	0·19	9·5	0·19
o-xylene ,,	8·5	0·51	10·5	0·53
Chloroform (in heptane)	2·4	1·23	3·4	1·10
Camphor ,,	6·8	2·97	7·1	2·98

A special interest of both these procedures lies in their ability to reveal moments beneath, say, 0·4D. As explained before (p. 15), such small magnitudes cannot dependably be ascertained *via* polarization and refractivity data (cf. *Dielectrics*, pp. 125, 163).

(6) *Stark Splitting in Microwave Spectroscopy.* The recording of a microwave spectrum may be understood by imagining apparatus working as follows: an oscillator (such as a Klystron) feeds power down a wave-guide into which may be admitted at fractional millimetre pressures a gas whose absorption is to be studied. The frequency of the generator is varied synchronously with the horizontal sweep of an oscilloscope. The differences between the outputs of two detector crystals, one at the entrance and the other at the exit of the absorbing path, are made continuously to supply vertical deflections on the oscilloscope screen. Thus absorptions will be displayed as peaks rising from the trace obtained when the guide is evacuated.

The cause of absorption can be inferred from the fact that the energy equivalent of one quantum at, say, 24,000 megacycles/sec. (corresponding to a wave-length of 1·25 cm.) is $h\nu$, i.e.

$$6·62 \times 10^{-27} \times 24 \times 10^{9} = 1·59 \times 10^{-16} \text{ ergs}$$

(h is Planck's constant, and ν the frequency). Now for an ordinary linear molecule such as carbonylsulphide, O=C=S, the moment of inertia perpendicular to the axis is of the order 10^{-38} grm. cm.^{2} so that the energy separation between the first two rotational levels will be given by $h^2 \mathscr{J}(\mathscr{J}+1)/8\pi^2 . 10^{-38}$ ergs for the transition $\mathscr{J}=0$ to $\mathscr{J}=1$. This is about 0.6×10^{-16} erg. Micro-wave spectra are therefore concerned with molecular rotation.

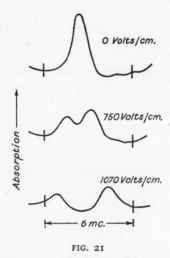

FIG. 21

High resolving power is an advantageous characteristic of this technique; spectral lines as close as 4×10^{-6} cm.$^{-1}$ (140 kilocycles/sec.) have been separated (compared with perhaps 0.1 cm.$^{-1}$ with the best infra-red spectrographs). Fortunately also the measurement of frequency can be made with high accuracy (*ca.* 1 in 10^6 at 25,000 mc./sec.).

If now a D.C. field is imposed on the gas in such a spectrometer (e.g. by laying a thin strip of metal along and insulated from the top length of the wave-guide) the single absorption peak due to a pure rotational transition will 'split' into two, one appearing at a higher and the other at a lower frequency than the maximum for the unperturbed (i.e. with applied field = zero) transition. Fig. 21 illustrates the phenomena with the 24,320 mc./sec. 'line' of carbonylsulphide (see Dakin, Good, and Coles, *Physical Rev.*, 1946, **70**, 560).

The frequency separation is proportional to the squares of both the field and the dipole moment, as well as to the moment of inertia, and the quantum numbers of the transition under observation. When the last two quantities are known for a molecule, its dipole moment can be ascertained. The figure obtained is the true μ_{gas}, i.e. the value uncomplicated by solvent interactions or by deviations from the ideal gas law.

The following table compares results with those from the older dielectric constant method:

Gas	μ_{gas} (Stark)	μ_{gas} (ε Method)
O:C:S	0·7085±0·004D (a)	0·65, 0·720D (b)
N_2O	0·166±0·002 (c)*	0·17 (b)
CH_3Cl	1·869±0·010 (c)*	1·86 (d)
CH_3Br	1·797±0·015 (c)*	1·82 (e)
CH_3I	1·647±0·014 (c)*	1·64 (b)
SO_2	1·59±0·01 (f)*	1·62 (g)
CH_2O	2·17 (h)	2·27 (i)
$(CH_2)_2O$	1·88±0·01 (j)*	1·89 (k)

* Determined relatively to OCS.

References: (a) Shulman and Townes, *Physical Rev.*, 1950, **77**, 500; (b) M.I.T. Tables; (c) Schulman, Dailey and Townes, *Physical Rev.*, 1950, **78**, 145; (d) Barclay and Le Fèvre, *J.C.S.*, 1950, 556; (e) Buckingham and Le Fèvre, unpublished; (f) Crable and Smith, *J. Chem. Physics*, 1951, **19**, 502; (g) Le Fèvre, Ross and Smythe, *J.C.S.*, 1950, 276; (h) Bragg and Sharbaugh, *Physical Rev.*, 1949, **75**, 1774; (i) Hurdis and Smyth, *J. Amer. Chem. Soc.*, 1943, **65**, 89; (j) Cunningham *et al.*, *J. Chem. Physics*, 1951, **19**, 676; (k) Angyal, Barclay and Le Fèvre, *J.C.S.*, 1950, 3370.

In general it is seen that the agreement is close. It may be noted that for carbonylsulphide, which is tending to be adopted as a standard in relative determinations, at least two higher moments *via* Stark splitting (0.72 and $0.732D$) have been published. However, the method, although at present essentially restricted to fairly simple polar molecules, is topically undergoing intensive development.

The apparatus requisite for microwave spectroscopy is, of course, much more intricate than indicated at the opening of this section; detailed descriptions may be found in the literature (e.g. Schulman and Townes, *Physical Rev.*, 1950, **77**, 500, or Sharbaugh, *Rev. Sci. Instr.*, 1950, **21**, 120).

A review of the whole subject up to 1948 is given by Gordy (*Rev. Mod. Physics*, 1948, **20**, 668).

GENERAL REFERENCES

Weissberger, *Physical Methods of Organic Chemistry*, Interscience Publishers, New York, 1945, Vol. II, Chap. XX.

Dielectrics, A General Discussion published by the Faraday Society as Vol. XLIIA of their *Transactions* for 1946.

Whiffen, 'Rotation Spectra', *Quarterly Revs.*, 1950, **4**, 131.

Together with the three books cited at end of Chapter I.

CHAPTER III

SOLVENT EFFECTS IN DIPOLE MOMENT MEASUREMENTS

H. MÜLLER (*Physikal Z.*, 1933, **34**, 689; *Trans. Far. Soc.*, 1934, **30**, 731) was the first clearly to show that electric moments obtained from measurements made with solutions are liable to vary with the nature of the solvents used and to deviate from the true moments found in the gaseous state. Two general causes for this behaviour are obvious: (1) the forces which dissolved molecules exert upon one another—*association* in its broadest sense, and (2) the effects of the non-polar solvent on the molecules of polar solute—*solvation*. In a series of solutions of the same substance the influence of (1) should diminish as dilution proceeds and may actually be eliminated in the final $_\infty P_2$ value; general information on this point is obtainable by considering the many published observations on gases. These show that at pressures of the order of one atmosphere the theoretical formulae, such as (4), are accurately obeyed, and since these do not take account of association between the molecules it must be concluded that this is negligible. Therefore—assuming that the extrapolation to infinite dilution is correct and that no systematic errors are connected with the processes of measurement—it can justifiably be inferred that solution data are not vitiated by association effects when the solute molecules are on the average as separated as they would be under ordinary gaseous conditions. The lower concentrations at which solution measurements are sometimes made correspond to pressures of a few millimetres. For these, therefore, and the derived $_\infty P_2$ figures, only solvation effects need be considered; in pure liquids and concentrated solutions (1) and (2) will be operating together.

The measurements made by Müller himself are summarized in Fig. 22.

It is noticeable that the gradation in steepness of the curves runs parallel to the magnitudes of the moments

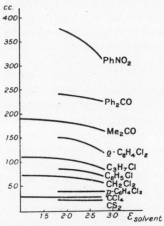

FIG. 22.—Variation of $_{\infty}P_2$ with dielectric constant of solvent

of the solutes examined, nitrobenzene ($\mu = 4D$) being the steepest and p-dichlorobenzene, carbon tetrachloride, and carbon disulphide—all non-polar molecules—being actually horizontal. It is therefore likely that the solvation effect is connected with the *moment*, either directly as such or indirectly as the orientation polarization. Proceeding in this way, Müller found that the $_oP$ values for the majority of the above substances could be accommodated on a single curve when their relative magnitudes with respect to the gaseous state were plotted against the dielectric constant of the solvent. This curve was defined empirically by the formula:

$$_oP_{\text{solution}}/_oP_{\text{gas}} = 1 - (0.075 \pm 0.005)(\varepsilon - 1)^2.$$

Its general applicability failed, however, conspicuously in the cases of ketones.

Shortly after the publication of the above work, Jenkins (*Nature*, 1934, **133**, 106) reported that for nitrobenzene in a number of solvents, $_\infty P_2$ is a linear function of $1/\varepsilon$ or $_\infty P_2 = K_1 + K_2/\varepsilon$, where $K_{1 \text{ and } 2}$ are constants; while Sugden (*Nature*, 1934, **133**, 415) showed that for several substances the polarization of the solute at any concentration is simply related to the *volume polarization* $(\varepsilon-1)/(\varepsilon+2) = \theta$ of the *solution*, i.e.

$$P_2 = (\text{constant}) - _0P\theta = x + P_{\text{gas}} - _0P\theta.$$

According to Snoek (*Trans. Far. Soc.*, 1934, **30**, 721), the last formula is essentially identical with one he and Arkel had suggested earlier.

From 1934 onwards the problem of the dependence of the apparent moment of a substance on its state (i.e. whether liquid, dissolved, or gaseous) has continued to receive attention. The various treatments may be roughly divided into four classes: (*a*) the devising of simple correlations between polarization and $\varepsilon_{\text{solvent}}$, (*b*) the introduction of factors, sometimes empirical, for solute and/or for medium, not included in the Clausius-Mosotti-Debye approach, (*c*) restarting the calculation of dielectric polarization from new fundamental premises, and (*d*) the addition to the proposals under (*b*) and (*c*) of the conception of either hindered rotation or quasi-crystallinity in liquids.

Class (*a*) includes the equations, already mentioned, of Müller, Jenkins, Arkel and Snoek, and Sugden, together with others advanced about the same time (see Glasstone, *Ann. Reports*, 1936, **33**, 117). They all forecast that apparent moments in solution should be *smaller* than the corresponding values determined for the same solutes as gases. Such a relationship was indeed observed in the majority of the cases where both μ_{gas} and

$\mu_{solution}$ were known; subsequently, however, a minority of compounds (e.g. certain trialkylamines, paraldehyde, chloroform, &c.) were found for which $\mu_{solution}$ exceeded μ_{gas}. It thus became evident that no equation of type (a), having $\varepsilon_{solvent}$ as the only characteristic parameter, could be *generally* valid.

First in order of publication in class (b) was a paper by Weigle (*Helv. Physica Acta*, 1933, **6**, 68) in which were considered the polarization and the orientation of optically anisotropic solvent molecules surrounding a dipolar solute. The former effect is greater than the latter. Unfortunately Weigle developed his argument around a molecular model of special shape—a cone, with spherical base, terminated at its point by 'une calotte spherique d'ouverture θ'—to which few solutes can be convincingly fitted. However, approximately, the extra moment acting along the line of the primary moment is $B(b_1 + 2b_2)\mu_{gas}/3$, where b_1 and b_2 are the polarizabilities along the two axes of the solvent molecule, which is taken as an ellipsoid of rotation. Values of b_1 and b_2 are accessible from the 'Kerr' effect (see Stuart and Volkmann, *Ann. Physik*, 1933, **18**, 140). The constant B contains $\cos \theta$ and may therefore be positive or negative; its magnitude varies with the dimensions of the particular sphere and cone assumed to represent the dissolved molecule.

Weigle's calculations were therefore of the requisite form to predict correctly that, dependently on the structure of the solute, μ_{gas} may not always exceed $\mu_{solution}$.

Both Higasi (*Sci. Papers Inst. Phys. Chem. Res. Tokyo*, 1936, **28**, 284) and Frank (*Proc. Roy. Soc.*, 1935, **152A**, 171) resemble Weigle in their approach to the problem: when a polarizable medium contains a polar molecule the latter sets up an induced polarization in the former which is fixed relatively to the primary dipole and being independent of any motion of the medium must be vectorially combined with the primary moment. Thus the apparent moment in solution

$$= \mu_{\text{solution}} = \mu_{\text{gas}} + \Sigma \mu_{\text{induced}}.$$

Higasi stresses the importance of the shape of the solute molecule and adopts as a general model an ellipsoid of revolution with a dipole at the centre along its axis of symmetry. Two cases are at once obvious: (1) where the radius (a) along the axis of symmetry is greater than that (c) along the axis perpendicular to it, and (2) where the reverse applies, viz. where $a < c$. For (1) $\Sigma \mu_{\text{induced}} = 4\pi n \alpha \mu A$, whilst for (2)

$$\Sigma \mu_{\text{induced}} = 4\pi \alpha n \mu B,$$

where n, α, and μ represent respectively the number of solvent molecules in unit volume, polarizability of the solvent, and the dipole moment of the solute. A and B have the following values:

$$A = \frac{-1}{k^2 - 1} \left\{ 1 - \frac{k}{\sqrt{k^2 - 1}} \log \left[k + \sqrt{k^2 - 1} \right] \right\} - \frac{1}{3}$$

$$B = \frac{k'^2}{k'^2 - 1} \left\{ 1 - \frac{1}{\sqrt{k'^2 - 1}} \sin^{-1} \frac{\sqrt{k'^2 - 1}}{k'} \right\} - \frac{1}{3}$$

in which k and k' are parameters depending upon the shape of the solute molecules, e.g. for (1) $k = a/c$ and for (2) $k' = 1/k$.

Inspection of these formulae shows that their predictions can be summarized briefly by saying that the apparent moment of a substance in solution and as a gas will be related as follows: μ_{sol} is greater than, equal to, or less than μ_{gas} according as a is less than, equal to, or greater than c.

Frank illustrates his calculation of $\Sigma \mu_{\text{induced}}$ by reference to a model in which each polar solute molecule is surrounded by six non-polar solvent molecules, cubically packed in a continuous medium. His diagram is reproduced here (Fig. 23); the dipole molecule is shown in the middle and the induced moments indicated by dotted arrows. It is seen that four induced moments will oppose the primary moment and two will augment it, but as the latter are each twice as great as the former (cf. equations for induction), the net effect is zero, i.e. for ideally spherical molecules the solvent will not affect the moment.

As soon, however, as the symmetry of the arrangement is destroyed by introducing a solute molecule displacing some of the solvent, $\Sigma\mu_{induced}$ is no longer zero, but

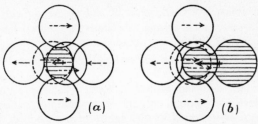

FIG. 23

will act to *reduce* the primary moment so that μ_{gas} becomes greater than $\mu_{solution}$. Similarly, displacement of solvent from positions in a plane at right angles to the dipole axis will lead to a value of $\Sigma\mu_{induced}$ acting in the same direction as the primary dipole and, by thus augmenting it, making μ_{gas} less than $\mu_{solution}$. Frank has generalized these conclusions in the form:

$$\Delta\mu = (A_1 + A_2)\mu_{gas}(\varepsilon - 1)/\varepsilon,$$

where $\Delta\mu$ is the change of moment observed going from gas to solution measurements, A_1 and A_2 are constants depending upon molecular geometry and certain external boundary conditions, while ε is the dielectric constant of the solvent.

Some years before the publications just mentioned, Raman and Krishnan (*Proc. Roy. Soc.*, 1928, **117A**, 589) had proposed modifications to the Clausius-Mosotti expression, the chief being to recognize the electrical and optical anisotropy of the molecules, the terms Θ and Ψ respectively, being introduced for this purpose. Goss (*Trans. Far. Soc.*, 1934, **30**, 751) was the first to utilize this work in the present problem by noting that if Sugden's relation were cast into the form:

$$P = A + B(\varepsilon - 1)/(\varepsilon + 2)$$

and compared with the equation of Raman and Krishnan, the constants acquire the values

$$A = {}_EP + {}_AP + {}_OP \text{ and } B = N\Psi + N\Theta/3kT$$

The anisotropy coefficients Ψ and Θ are difficult to evaluate; for most *gaseous* substances they are small, and accordingly the theoretical expression

$$P = {}_EP + {}_AP + {}_OP$$

is nearly accurate.

Since, following Müller, it seemed that for a given substance in solution only the orientation polarization is measurably affected by the nature of the medium, the constant Ψ was ignored by Le Fèvre and Le Fèvre (*J.C.S.*, 1935, 1747) and a simple expression for the ratio of the orientation polarizations in the dissolved and gaseous states obtained

$$_OP_{\text{solution}}/_OP_{\text{gas}} = 1 + 3\Theta(\varepsilon - 1)/4\pi\mu^2(\varepsilon + 2).$$

A point of interest arose from this result: the sign of Θ is usually opposite to that of the Kerr constant which for the majority of compounds is positive; for these, therefore, Θ is negative and the ratio of polarizations fractional. For such cases the observed polarization at infinite dilution should be less than that for the vapour. On the other hand, the few compounds which exhibit *negative* Kerr constants should have relative polarizations in the reverse sense.

Roughly speaking, the last forecast is realized in fact, although a few isolated exceptions have appeared since 1935. The sign of Θ may not *always* be the reverse of that of the Kerr constant; moreover, the Le Fèvres certainly over-simplified the Raman-Krishnan expression (cf. Jenkins and Bauer, *J. Amer. Chem. Soc.*, 1936, **58**, 2435).

Unfortunately neither of the previous two methods permitted an easy *a priori* calculation of $_oP_{soln}/_oP_{gas}$ (i.e. μ^2_{soln}/μ^2_{gas}). The work of Goss (*J.C.S.*, 1937, 1915; cf. also *ibid.*, 1940, 753) provides one route by which this may be done. Goss found that for certain polar solutes in the isotropic solvent, carbon tetrachloride, the variation of their partial molar polarizations ($P_{partial}$) in the polarizations, P_{12}, of the mixtures, could be expressed as:

$$P_{partial} = {}_DP + Z(\varepsilon_{12}-1)^4/(\varepsilon_{12}+2)^4 + Y/\varepsilon_{12}.$$

At infinite dilution, when $P_{partial} = {}_\infty P_2$, and $\varepsilon_{12} = \varepsilon_1$, the second term becomes negligible, making Y/ε_1 nearly equal to $_oP_{soln}$. Moreover, it was shown experimentally that $(Y - {}_oP_{gas})({}_DP)^{\frac{1}{3}}/_oP_{gas}[(Z+{}_DP)^{\frac{1}{3}} - ({}_DP)^{\frac{1}{3}}]$ had an average value for several substances of 3, so that $_oP_{soln}/_oP_{gas} = \{3[(Z+{}_DP)/_DP]^{\frac{1}{3}} - 2\}/\varepsilon_1$. The quantity Z is connected with the dimensions, b_1, b_2, and b_3, of the polarizability ellipsoid for the solute molecule *via* $K = 2b_1/(b_2+b_3) = 6\cdot55 - 3\cdot82[(Z+{}_DP)/_DP]^{\frac{1}{3}}$, where b_1 is taken as the polar axis.

In the following five examples, polarizability data for b_1, b_2, and b_3 from Stuart (*Molekülstruktur*, 1934, p. 221) have been used to estimate μ_{gas} from the values of μ_{CCl_4} listed in the M.I.T. Tables:

Substance	μ (*in* CCl_4)	μ_{gas} (*calc.*)	μ_{gas} (*found*)
C_6H_5Cl	1·64, 1·65	1·76, 1·77	1·73
$C_6H_5NO_2$	various from 3·93 to 4·02	4·36–4·46	4·24
Me_2CO	2·70	2·72	various from 2·85 to 3·02
$CHCl_3$	1·10, 1·15	1·03, 1·07	1·01
Et_2O	1·24	1·18	1·17

The agreement is seen to be close.

Turning now to the approaches under class (c) we may note that neither the Clausius-Mosotti-Debye formulae nor any of the modifications given so far apply well to pure polar liquids. Writing $_oP_{liq}$ for the difference between $_TP_{liq}$ and R we have (where ε, d, and n^2 are measurements on the liquid):

$$_oP_{liq} = {_TP_{liq}} - R = 3M(\varepsilon - n^2)/(\varepsilon + 2)(n^2 + 2)d.$$

Taking $_oP_{liq}$ as $4\pi N\mu^2_{liq}/9kT$ often yields figures for μ_{liq} which are markedly different from the correct values, μ_{gas}, obtained in the gaseous phase (e.g. for $PhNO_2$, $\mu_{gas} = 4\cdot24$, $\mu_{liq} = 1\cdot7D$, for $PhCl$, $\mu_{gas} = 1\cdot73$, $\mu_{liq} = 1\cdot15D$. Better agreement is shown by $CHCl_3$, $\mu_{gas} = 1\cdot01$, $\mu_{liq} = 0\cdot98D$, or ether, $\mu_{gas} = 1\cdot17$, $\mu_{liq} = 1\cdot25D$).

Henriquez (Rec. trav. chim., 1935, 54, 574) attempted an empirical remedy as follows: suppose that the force, previously called F_2, acting at the centre of the spherical cavity assumed on p. 9, is not simply $4\pi U/3$, but this multiplied by a constant a; accordingly, the molecular polarization of the dielectric becomes

$$M(\varepsilon - 1)/[3 + a(\varepsilon - 1)]d.$$

The value of a, found by comparison with extant data, is approximately: $a = 1 - (\varepsilon - 1)/(\varepsilon + 4)$, from which $_TP_{liq}$ becomes $(\varepsilon - 1)(\varepsilon + 4)/M(8\varepsilon + 7)d$. The orientation polarization is then

$$_oP_{liq} = 4\pi N\mu^2/9kT = \frac{M}{d}\left[\frac{(\varepsilon - 1)(\varepsilon + 4)}{8\varepsilon + 7} - \frac{(n^2 - 1)(n^2 + 4)}{8n^2 + 7}\right];$$

where ε is greater than 20 Henriquez adds $1\cdot7(\varepsilon - 1)^3 \cdot 10^{-3}$ to the denominator of the dielectric constant term. The equation yields estimates of μ_{gas} of the correct order, although its success is not uniform over a range of molecules, as the examples tabulated at the top of p. 77 show.

Onsager (J. Amer. Chem., Soc. 1936, 58, 1486) discarded the Clausius-Mosotti model completely. He assumed the molecules to be spherical and the neighbourhood of each

Substance	μ (calc.)	μ (found)
Chlorobenzene	1·60	1·73
Bromobenzene	1·50	1·71
Nitrobenzene	4·10	4·24
Acetophenone	3·33	3·02
Diethylether	1·47	1·17
Acetone	2·92	2·85 to 3·02
Ethyl bromide	1·89	2·01
Chloroform	1·38	1·01

solute molecule to be a continuum without discrete structure. Thus the field acting upon a molecule in a polarized dielectric can be analysed into a *cavity field G* (given by the shape of the molecule and proportional to the external field intensity) and a *reaction field R* (proportional to the total electric moment and depending on the instantaneous orientation of the molecule). The *mean* orientation of a molecule is determined by the force-couple exerted by G upon the electric moment of the molecule; but the electric moment of the molecule will be enhanced by the reaction field R and the induced moment due to the cavity field G will be similarly augmented by the corresponding component of R. From these premises the following equation is deduced for a pure polar liquid:

$$4\pi N\mu^2/9kT = M(\varepsilon - n^2)(2\varepsilon + n^2)/d\varepsilon(n^2 + 2)^2.$$

This has been tested on 31 pure liquids by Böttcher (*Physica*, 1939, **6**, 59), who finds it to give values for μ in accord with μ_{gas}. Examples have been discovered subsequently which are less satisfactory. Wilson (*Chem. Reviews*, 1939, **25**, 377), moreover, has criticized Onsager's neglect of association effects and of molecular anisotropy. He further suggests that instead of using for n the extrapolated value of the refractive index at infinite wave-length, an 'effective refractive index', defined by $(n^2_{eff} - 1)/(n^2_{eff} + 2) = d(_EP + _AP)/M$ should be taken, where $(_EP + _AP)$ is the observed distortion polarization (preferably from gas measurements).

Wilson has adapted Onsager's theory to cover the

anisotropy of the molecular units forming a liquid: if n_1 is the effective refractive index corresponding to the polarizability b_1 along the dipole axis (defined by an equation similar to that just written), and if n is the average effective refractive index, then

$$M(\varepsilon-n^2)/d\varepsilon(2\varepsilon+n^2)=4\pi N\mu^2(n_1^2+2)^2/9kT(2\varepsilon+n_1^2)^2,$$

n_1 being estimated from Kerr constant polarizability data. That this adjustment was in the right direction was demonstrated by Wilson by plotting the ratios $\mu^2_{\text{calc}}/\mu^2_{\text{gas}}$ against temperature. With increase of T such graphs should obviously approach unity: they did this *only* when μ_{calc} was deduced *via* the revised equation.

Where association is concerned, Onsager's equation has been modified by Kirkwood (*J. Chem. Phys.*, 1939, **7**, 911; *Ann. N.Y. Acad. Sci.*, 1940, **40**, 315), who has allowed, in principle, for a mutual action of any kind between the molecules, although—since this action cannot yet be evaluated in precise terms—the equation he derives is not amenable to direct test. Kirkwood finds:

$$M(\varepsilon-1)(2\varepsilon+1)/9\varepsilon d = {}_EP+{}_AP+4\pi N\mu\bar{\mu}/9kT$$
$$= {}_EP+{}_AP+4\pi N\mu^2 g/9kT,$$

where μ is the dipole moment of the molecule in the absence of an applied field, and is evaluated sufficiently accurately by the relation, due to Onsager,

$$\mu=\frac{2\varepsilon+1}{2\varepsilon+n^2}\cdot\frac{n^2+2}{3}\cdot\mu_0.$$

Kirkwood's $\bar{\mu}$ is the total moment of a molecule and its neighbours in the region surrounding it, in which the local dielectric constant differs effectively from the overall macroscopic value.

The 'correlation parameter', g, is a measure of the degree and strength of association of the molecules in the liquid. Values, from experiment, for a few well-known substances are:

Sulphur dioxide (25°):	$g=1.4$	Ammonia (15°):	$g=1.3$
Water (25°)	2.68	Ether (20°)	1.7
Ethanol (20°)	3.0	Acetone (20°)	1.1
HCN (20°)	4.1	Nitrobenzene (20°)	1.1
HF (0°)	3.1	Ethyl bromide (20°)	1.1
		Pyridine (20°)	0.9

Were it possible to calculate g a priori, then μ (i.e. the true moment, μ_{gas}) could be secured from observations of ε, d, and n on the liquid. Unfortunately this does not yet seem to have been done with certainty (see Frenkel, *Kinetic Theory of Liquids*, Oxford, 1946).

Onsager himself extended his original equation to cover solutions of polar solutes in non-polar solvents; Oster (*J. Amer. Chem. Soc.*, 1946, **68**, 2036) has dealt similarly with the expression of Kirkwood, and made an interesting study (which cannot be described here) of the concentration dependence of g. Wilson, although allowing for anisotropy, retained Onsager's supposition of spherical molecules. Ross and Sack (*Proc. Phys. Soc.*, 1950, **63**, 893) therefore carried the subject a stage further by treating a *solute* molecule as a uniform *ellipsoid*, having an isotropic refractive index n (defined in relation to $_DP$ in the same way as Wilson's n_{eff}) surrounded by an isotropic continuum with a dielectric constant ε equal to that of the solvent in bulk.

Ultimately they deduce that

$$\mu_{soln}/\mu_{gas} = \frac{3\varepsilon[1+(n^2-1)\xi]}{(\varepsilon+2)[\varepsilon+(n^2-\varepsilon)\xi]}$$

Here ξ is an 'internal field function' by which the internal field in an *ellipsoidal cavity* is $F=E+4\pi\xi P$ (instead of $E+4\pi P/3$ as assumed for a *spherical* cavity on p. 9; its calculation involves the theory of ellipsoidal harmonics in association with Jacobian elliptic functions, but (considerably) Ross and Sack have summarized many such computations graphically, and appropriate values of ξ can be read directly from Fig. 1

of their paper, provided that the dimensions (or polarizabilities) of the solute molecule are available.

The applicability of the equation is illustrated by the following examples from among those quoted by Ross and Sack:

Substance	SO_2	CH_3Cl	$CHCl_3$
$\mu_{soln} \cdot \mu_{gas}$ (calc.)*	0·99	0·94	1·02
ditto (observed)*	1·00	0·91	1·12

Substance	$(CH_3)_2CO$	C_6H_5Cl	$C_6H_5NO_2$
μ_{soln}/μ_{gas} (calc.)*	0·96$_5$	0·88	0·97
ditto (observed)*	0·95	0·90	0·93

* Solvent=benzene

To date, the μ_{soln}/μ_{gas} ratio known most greatly to exceed unity is that (1·30) for paraldehyde (*J.C.S.*, 1950, 290); the relation just discussed forecasts 1·25; it is—in short—the most satisfactory yet produced of those which rest upon *a priori* theory.

Turning now to the proposals classified under (d), it is evident that the dielectric properties and the structures of liquids are related problems in that a solution of the second would give a model upon which to calculate the first. Stewart's idea of cybotaxis (*Rev. Mod. Physics*, 1930, **2**, 116; *Physical Rev.*, 1931, **37**, 9), and the experimental evidence behind it, seems particularly suggestive, since the predisposition of a liquid to contain more or less ordered arrangements over small elements of its volume implies anisotropic properties for the molecules concerned. Debye (*Physik. Z.*, 1935, **36**, 100, 193; *Chem. Revs.*, 1936, **19**, 171) and Fowler (*Proc. Roy. Soc.*, 1935, **149A**, 1) have assumed that dipolar molecules in liquids are not free to rotate but only to execute oscillations about axes whose directions change slowly, and which over short periods of time are fixed by the field of the neighbouring molecules. Thus Debye writes for the orientation polarization: $_oP=(4\pi N\mu^2/9kT)(1-L^2(\beta))$, where $L(\beta)$ is Langevin's function for $\beta = E/kT$. For SO_2 we have from experiment $_oP_{liq}/_oP_{gas} = 0.5 = [1 - L^2(\beta)]$, whence E, the 'binding energy' $= 3.4\ kT$; for comparison, water shows $_oP_{liq}/_oP_{gas} = 0.193$ and $E = 11kT$, and ammonia, 0.41 and $4.4\ kT$ respectively. The theoretical calculation of E has not yet been accomplished. Attempts, using the molecular interactions obtained by London (*Trans. Far. Soc.*, 1937, **33**, 8) in conjunction with inter-dipole distances of $2r$, where $r^3 = 0.916 \times$ molecular volume $\times 10^{-24}$ yield only $E = 0.25\ kT$ for H_2O and $0.1\ kT$ for NH_3. A more serious objection is that the factor $(1 - L^2(\beta))$ fails to deal with cases (e.g. paraldehyde, NMe_3, &c.) where $_oP_{liq}/_oP_{gas}$ exceeds unity.

Kincaid and Eyring (*J. Chem. Physics*, 1938, **6**, 620) have approached the question *via* the 'free volumes' and the 'free angle ratios' of molecules in a condensed phase. Both these concepts, to a first approximation, concern the regions in which displacement can occur. For molecules with three degrees of freedom the f.a.r. is written δ_3 and the rotation taken as restricted between the limits of the polar angles 0 and θ_1, then

$$\mu^2_{liq}/\mu^2_{gas} = 1 - [(1 + \cos\theta_1)/2]^2.$$

Since it is often approximately true that the potential curves for the rotation of the molecule about the three axes are symmetrical, $\delta_2 = \delta_3^{2/3}$ and $\delta_2 = (1 - \cos\theta_1)/2$. For the angular water molecule, $1/\delta_3$ is calculable—from the product (6.1×10^{-120}) of the principal moments of inertia and various constants—as

$$10.14 \times 10^{60} \times (ABC)^{\frac{1}{2}} = 25.05;$$

δ_2 therefore is 0.116, whence

$$\mu^2_{liq}/\mu^2_{gas} = _oP_{liq}/_oP_{gas} = 0.22,$$

i.e. of the order found by direct measurement (0.19). Despite the agreement displayed in this case, however, the methods of Kincaid and Eyring cannot, in their present form, correctly forecast those circumstances which lead to oP_{liq}/oP_{gas} ratios greater than one.

None of the empirical or theoretical approaches so far discussed adequately embraces *all* the known facts concerning the effects of the medium in dipole moment measurements. Some seem valid for the difference between $\mu_{solution}$ and μ_{gas} but fail when tested on pure polar liquids, others—especially produced for polar liquids—are unable to cover *all* such liquids. Since 'true' dipole moments can only be obtained by measurements on gases at low pressures (i.e. when the underlying theory is strictly applicable), and because many substances may be dissolved but cannot be vaporized without decomposition, the problem of calculating μ_{gas} from $\mu_{solution}$ becomes a practical one whenever it is desired to compare accurately the dipole moments of volatilizable and non-volatilizable compounds.

Accordingly reference may be made to an equation (Buckingham and Le Fèvre, *J.C.S.*, 1952, 1932), devised empirically, of the form:

$$\mu^2_{soln}/\mu^2_{gas} = 1 + A^*(\varepsilon_1 - 1)/(\varepsilon_1 + 2) - B^*,$$

where
$$A^* = e^{x^2} - (e - e^{x^2})3(n_1^2 - n_2^2)(1 - ex^2)^2$$

and
$$B^* = \frac{1 \cdot 69 e^{x^2}(\varepsilon_1 - 1)|\varepsilon_1 - n_2^2|(n_2^2 + 1)}{\varepsilon_1^2 n_2^2 (e^{x^2} + 1)(e^{M_2/d_2} ABC)}$$

in which ε, n, M, and d stand for the dielectric constant, refractive index, molecular weight and density respectively, and subscripts 1 and 2 for the solvent or solute; e is 2·7183, the base of Napierian logarithms. The shape of the solute molecule is recognized in e^{x^2}, which is obtained from scale drawings, based on known interatomic distances, valency angles, &c., upon which the 'Wirkungsradien' of Stuart (*Z. physikal. Chem.*, 1935, **B 27**, 350) have been superimposed. If A is the dimension along the axis of $\mu_{\text{resultant}}$, and C is the lesser of the other two measurements perpendicular to A, then generally $x^2 = (C^2 - A^2)/(\text{greatest length})^2$; e^{x^2} is thus essentially concerned with areas, and could be a measure of hindrance to rotation, so that it (or its difference from unity) may reflect the non-randomness of rotational modes about the greatest and least axis of length of the solute molecule, and the factor $(e - e^{x^2})$ the degree of elongation of the molecule in a direction at right angles to its dipole axis.

For a pure polar liquid, A^* in the relation $\mu^2_{\text{liquid}}/\mu^2_{\text{gas}}$ becomes simply $(e^{x^2} - 1)$. When the solvent is non-polar, and ε_1 is close to n_2^2, the term B^* is small and can, in estimating $\mu^2_{\text{solution}}/\mu^2_{\text{gas}}$, often be neglected. The following examples illustrate the use of these equations to 'correct' apparent moments, deduced from observations on solutions or the pure liquid, to the true (or gas) values:

	μ_{C6H6}	μ_{gas} (calc.)	μ_{liq}	μ_{gas} (calc.)	μ_{gas} (observe d)
CH_3Cl	1·69	1·85	1·19	1·96	1·86
CH_2Cl_2	1·55	1·57	1·14$_5$	1·58	1·57
$CHCl_3$	1·13	1·01	0·97$_5$	0·98	1·01
$(CH_3)_2CO$	2·74	2·87	1·52	3·04	2·85–3·02
Paraldehyde	1·87	1·48	1·74$_5$	1·65	1·44
C_6H_5Cl	1·59	1·72	1·15	1·67	1·73
$C_6H_5NO_2$	3·95	4·25	1·69	4·24	4·24
C_6H_5CN	4·05	4·41	1·71	4·31	4·39

Further illustrations, and also comparisons of the predictions possible from the same basic data by the Onsager or Ross-Sack relations, are listed in the paper by Buckingham and Le Fèvre; they demonstrate the superiority of the formulae proposed by the last-named pair and justify the claim that a method, useful in practice, is now available for estimating μ_{gas} from either u_{solution} or μ_{liquid}.

GENERAL REFERENCES

Glasstone, *Annual Reports*, 1936, **33**, 117

Van Vleck, *Annals of the New York Acad. of Sciences*, 1940, **40**, 293

Smith, *Science Progress*, 1948, **36**, 483

CHAPTER IV

DIPOLE MOMENTS AND MOLECULAR STRUCTURE

BY the methods outlined above the *resultant* dipole moment of the molecule is obtained. Examination of data relating to a few simple substances will show that electric polarity is a property associated with the chemical bonds between atoms and can be treated as a directed (vector) quantity:

N_2	0	CS_2	0	HCN	2·6
Cl_2	0	COS	0·71	NH_3	1·46
CO	0·12	H_2O	1·84	CH_4	0
HCl	1·08	H_2S	0·89	CCl_4	0
CO_2	0	SO_2	1·62	$SiCl_4$	0

Thus all diatomic molecules of the type AA are non-polar, because they are electrically symmetrical, whilst those of the type AB have a finite permanent moment because in them the bonding electrons are more under the influence of the atom with the larger positive nucleus. As an example the covalent link between hydrogen and chlorine in gaseous hydrogen chloride can be considered; here the halogen atom has the larger positive nucleus and accordingly the electrons of the hydrogen will be more attracted by the chlorine atom than will those of the halogen by the hydrogen. The link $H \longmapsto Cl$ will, therefore, be dipolar, with the dipole moment disposed as indicated, the hydrogen being positive and the chlorine negative. For this reason all hydrogen compounds of general formula HA will be dipolar with the hydrogen bearing a $\partial +$charge.

Molecules containing more than one polar link may, therefore, be either polar or non-polar, depending on the dispositions in space of the constituent link moments. *If a molecule has central symmetry it will be non-polar*, i.e. the constituent link moments will balance in the resultant. Thus simply by regarding the polarities of links as vector quantities we can forecast qualitatively the polarities of molecules:

Diatomic Molecules	Forecast	Examples
A_2	non-polar	N_2, O_2, &c.
AB	polar	HCl, CO, &c.

Triatomic Molecules		
ABA (rectilinear)	non-polar	CO_2, CS_2
ABA (triangular)	polar	H_2O, SO_2
ABC (linear)	polar	OCS, HCN

Tetra-atomic Molecules		
AB_3 (plane triangular with A at centre)	non-polar	BCl_3
AB_3 (triangular pyramid with A at apex)	polar	NH_3, $AsCl_3$

Penta-atomic Molecules		
AB_4 (tetrahedral grouping around A)	non-polar	CH_4, $SnCl_4$

These predictions agree with the experimental results in all cases where the molecular configuration is known.

It is important to notice that where carbon compounds are concerned the conclusions are in accord with classical stereochemistry. Thus the zero moments of methane and carbon tetrachloride are compatible with the existence in these molecules of four link moments inclined at 109° 28' to each other. This arrangement is symmetrical and the components, therefore, balance one another in the resultant. Similarly carbon dioxide and carbon disulphide must be expected to be rectilinear with the carbon atoms midway between the other two; for such formulae the theoretical resultant is zero. On the other hand, the molecules C:O and O:C:S should exhibit finite resultant moments in agreement with the experimental observations.

Equally in harmony with structural theory were the results of Errera (1925) for the isomeric dihalogeno-ethylenes. The moments of these substances were measured in benzene solution and $_E P + _A P$ eliminated by parallel dielectric constant and density observations for the solid state. The moments found are given beneath the formulae:

H—C—Cl H—C—Cl H—C—Br H—C—Br
‖ ‖ ‖ ‖
Cl—C—H H—C—Cl Br—C—H H—C—Br

Trans   *cis*   *Trans*   *cis*
$\mu = 0$ $\mu = 1 \cdot 89 D$ $\mu = 0$ $\mu = 1 \cdot 35 D$

H—C—I H—C—I
‖ ‖
I—C—H H—C—I

Trans   *cis*
$\mu = 0$ $\mu = 0 \cdot 76 D$

They show again how central symmetry implies zero moment and will serve to indicate the manner in which dipole moments can be applied to the resolution of structural questions.

A Practical Criterion of Non-polarity. From equation (4) it can be seen that when the resultant molecular moment is zero, the orientation polarization, given by $4 \pi N \mu^2 / 9 k T$, also disappears, leaving the total polarization equal to the sum of the electronic and atomic polarizations. This sum is expressed approximately by the molecular refraction, so that:

$$\frac{\varepsilon - 1}{\varepsilon + 2} \cdot \frac{M}{d} = \frac{n^2 - 1}{n^2 + 2} \cdot \frac{M}{d}, \text{ i.e. } \varepsilon = n^2.$$

If, therefore, it is found that a substance has a dielectric constant, measured in the ordinary way at audio or radio frequencies, which is roughly equal to the square of the refractive index, observed with visible light at the same temperature, the conclusion can be drawn that the compound has no moment. The method has special weight when the component moments are known to be high, e.g. those for the C—Cl or C—NO_2 links. Some illustrations are given in the following table:

Substance	Moment	ε	n^2_D
Carbon tetrachloride	0	2·18	2·13
Tetranitromethane	0	2·13	2·08
Benzene	0	2·27	2·24
Chloroform	1·0	4·72	2·08
Water	1·8	ca. 80	1·78
Ethyl alcohol	1·7	ca. 25	1·85
Nitrobenzene	4·0	ca. 35	2·40

The Quantitative Significance of the Dipole Moment. As the determinations of dipole moment to be placed on record accumulated it became obvious that homologous series of compounds had characteristic values which were fairly constant after the first one or two members. The following list is taken from a review by Bennett (*Annual Reps.*, 1929, **26**, 128); it shows the values then ascribed to members of the series named:

Alkyl chlorides	$\mu=2\cdot1$	Aldehydes	$\mu=2\cdot7$
,,　　bromides	1·9	Nitriles	3·4
,,　　iodides	1·85	Aliphatic amines:	
Alcohols	1·68	primary	1·3
Ethers	1·2	secondary	1·0
Ketones	2·73	tertiary	0·76

Since all saturated hydrocarbons had been found to be non-polar, the approximate uniformity of moment throughout a derived homologous series was therefore obviously attributable to *that* link, necessarily polar and common to all members, created by the substitution of a hydrogen atom in a hydrocarbon molecule by another atom or group. In the earliest discussions the dipole moment was treated as a property associated with the substituent group; being a vector quantity it was, however, also possible to calculate the resultant moment of a molecule containing several characteristic groups by a process analogous to that in which forces are compounded according to the parallelogram rule into a resultant. To this end certain data were required: the disposition of the groups in the molecular space formula, the appropriate 'group-moment' values, and their signs (by which can be indicated algebraically the directions in which the charges were distributed between the groups and the carbon atoms holding them).

Information on the last point was obtainable by a method suggested by Sir J. J. Thomson (*Phil. Mag.*, 1923, **46**, 407): The dipole moments of a number of substituted benzenes were considered on the assumption that the benzene skeleton is planar and hexagonally symmetrical even after substitution. The relative signs of the component moments were, therefore, revealed when the *observed* resultant was compared with that calculated. For example, both *p*-dichlorobenzene and *p*-xylene have zero moment, but *p*-chlorotoluene exhibits a moment of 1·9 units; this is roughly the *sum* of the moments of toluene and chlorobenzene. It is concluded, therefore, that the link moments C—Me and C—Cl act in different directions so that in *p*-chlorotoluene they augment one another. Instances where the substituents are in the *ortho-* or *meta-* positions can be dealt with by means of the formula:

$$(\text{Resultant})^2 = m_1^2 + m_2^2 + 2m_1m_2 \cos \theta,$$

where m_1 and m_2 are the component moments and θ is the angle at which they interact. Application of this procedure to a large number of cases made it obvious that the majority of links resembled the C—Halogen in sign. From what has been said above the halogen must form

7

the more negative element in the link and the results may be taken as indicating permanent electron shifts, e.g. in the molecules of toluene, chloro- and nitro-benzene in the directions shown:

$$\overset{\longleftarrow}{C_6H_5 \cdot Me} \qquad \overset{\longrightarrow}{C_6H_5 \cdot Hal} \qquad \overset{\longrightarrow}{C_6H_5 \cdot NO_2}$$
$$+\mu \qquad\qquad -\mu \qquad\qquad -\mu$$

Moments pointing *away* from the carbon atom are commonly designated negative, and *vice versa*. One of the first discussions of data along these lines was made by Williams (*Physikal. Z.*, 1929, **30**, 391), who gave the following series of group values:

.NO$_2$	$-3 \cdot 8D$	.Cl.	$-1 \cdot 5D$	.CO$_2$H	$-0 \cdot 9D$
.CHO	$-2 \cdot 8$	.Br	$-1 \cdot 5$	.CH$_3$	$+0 \cdot 4$
.OH	$-1 \cdot 7$	.OMe	$-1 \cdot 2$	.NH$_2$	$+1 \cdot 5$

This order was subjected to a certain amount of criticism; in particular Eucken and Meyer (*Physikal. Z.*, 1929, **30**, 397) maintained that it was not justifiable to take the resultant moment of a *group* —OR as acting along the bond between oxygen and the group R. They regarded the molecular resultant moment as the vector sum of *all* the single moments each collinear with a constituent bond in the molecule. To discover these a number of valency angles had to be assumed: that of dicovalent oxygen was taken to be 110° and carbon was regarded as tetrahedral. By analysis the following link moments were then evaluated:

C—C	H—O	C=O	CH$_3$—C	H—C	C—O	C—Cl
0	1·6	2·3	0·4	0·4	0·7	1·5

In many cases fair agreement with experimental results was obtained by the use of these data, e.g. the *calculated* values for phenol, *p*-chlorophenol and methyl chloride are 1·5, 2·3, and 1·9 respectively, as against the *found* values 1·6, 2·4, and 1·9 units.

Equally it seemed reasonable to use this procedure in reverse and, by knowing the component moments involved, to deduce from the polarity measured for the entire molecule containing them, their angle of interaction θ. One of the earliest applications of such an approach was to disubstituted benzenes; the isomers $C_6H_4Cl_2$ may be quoted in illustration: the dipole moments of o-, m-, and p-dichlorobenzenes were found experimentally to be 2·3, 1·48, and 0D respectively. Taking each component moment to be that for C—Cl (namely 1·5D) the three angles θ are calculable as 80°, 121°, and 180°. If the benzene ring were a regular hexagon with all substituents symmetrically placed, these values should be 60°, 120°, and 180°. Similar discrepancies between theory and experiment have been recorded for many *ortho*-compounds. It is obvious that the volumes of the 1:2-substituents *could* cause this effect, so too might electrostatic repulsive forces between two dipoles separated by the distances usual for 1:2-positions, but it is doubtful whether such groups are really splayed as widely as 80°; independent structure determinations *via* electron diffraction indicate angles for $o\text{-}C_6H_4Cl_2$ and $o\text{-}C_6H_4Br_2$ which are not seriously in excess of 60°, while the I—C—I angle in CH_2I_2 is only 115° compared with 112±2° for the corresponding angle in CH_2Cl_2 (cf. Allen and Sutton, *Acta Cryst.*, 1950, **3**, 46, for tabulated data on 500 molecules).

During the first decade or so of the use of dipole moments by chemists much effort was put into valency angle investigations on the above lines. Unfortunately few of the results can to-day be accepted as quantitatively certain. The reason for this lies with the assumptions beneath a 'table of link moments': (a) that the polarity of a given bond remains constant throughout a series of different molecules, and (b) that its magnitude is not affected by other polar links occurring in the same molecule. Then, if (a) and (b) are granted, the following are also required (c) preknowledge of the accurate geometries of the structure from which the table of link moments is to be drawn, and (d) dependable determinations of the resultant moments of all the molecules concerned—namely, of that to be analysed and of those to be treated under (c).

Apart from points (a) and (b) the data available on (c) to the earliest workers were often rough, and on (d) frequently limited to values of μ_{solution}.

The inadequacy of premise (b), and a possible method of correction, was first discussed by Smallwood and Herzfeld (*J. Amer. Chem. Soc.*, 1930, **52**, 1919) for the 1:2-disubstituted benzenes already mentioned. Two polar links, each μ_{C-X}, in proximity should *induce* moments one in the other, and depending on their mutual orientation the induced moments will act either to augment or reduce the primary moments. An approximate calculation of such induction is possible as follows: the moment induced in any substituent as the result of an electric intensity F is given by $\bar{m} = \alpha F$, where α is the polarizability (deformability) of the group. In the present case F is the force exerted on one dipolar link by the dipole of the other. If the dipole exerting the force F is situated at the origin of a set of plane polar coordinates, the horizontal and vertical components of F (F_x and F_y) at a point r length units distant are given by

$$F_x = \frac{x}{r^3}(3\cos^2\Theta - 1) + \frac{3y}{r^3}\sin\Theta\cos\Theta,$$

$$F_y = \frac{3x}{r^3}\sin\Theta\cos\Theta + \frac{y}{r^3}(3\sin^2\Theta - 1),$$

where x and y are the horizontal and vertical components of μ_{C-X}. The location of μ_{C-X} may be taken to be where the 'X-ray radii' of the atoms C and X meet on the line joining the centres of C and X. Numerical values of

α for such points can be obtained from octet refractions by the equation $\alpha = 3R_{octet}/4\pi N$, where N is Avogadro's number and $R_{octet} = R_{atom} + \frac{1}{4}R_{carbon}$; the following values are then calculated ($\times 10^{24}$):

—H	0·654	—I	5·46
—Cl	2·51	—CH$_3$	2·45
—Br	3·63	—NO$_2$	2·75

For application to the isomeric molecules $C_6H_4X_2$, the primary moment μ_{C-X} must first be found. This is done by fitting the related monosubstituted compound C_6H_5X into a set of axes so oriented that μ_{C-X} lies along the x axis; then the sum of the moments induced in the y directions will be zero by symmetry, and

$$(\mu_{C_6H_5X})_{observed} = \mu_{C-X} + \Sigma\mu_x.$$

In this case $\Sigma\mu_x$ is found on evaluation to be positive, but when the effect of one μ_{C-X} on another in the *ortho*-position is calculated, the corresponding term appears as algebraically negative, i.e. mutual induction is acting to reduce the primary moments.

Smallwood and Herzfeld followed the procedure just outlined with a large number of disubstituted benzenes, *taking the aromatic ring as a regular hexagon* holding its substituents on extended diagonals, and achieved estimates of the moments which were frequently close to the observed values, e.g.:

	$\mu_{observed}$	$\mu^*_{calc.}$ (S & H)
o-Dichlorobenzene	2·25	2·30
m- ,,	1·48	1·48
p- ,,	0	0

* Using $\mu_{C_6H_5Cl} = 1\cdot53D$ as recorded by Smyth, Morgan and Boyce (*J. Amer. Chem. Soc.*, 1928, **50**, 1536), to whom also are due the figures under $\mu_{observed}$.

It was evident therefore that Smallwood and Herzfeld had provided a valuable correction which diminished the apparent structural anomalies formerly reported for *ortho*-compounds.

Groves and Sugden (*J.C.S.*, 1937, 1992) later somewhat elaborated the calculation of $\Sigma\mu_{induced}$ in the groups attached to the main polar bond of simple compounds, such as CH_3Cl, CH_3CN, &c., whose moments they had measured as *gases*. The primary moments so found were presented as link moments, i.e. $(\mu_{gas})_{observed} = \mu_{link} + \Sigma\mu_{induced}$:

C—Cl	C—Br	C—I	C—O	C=O	C≡N	NO_2
1·87	1·80	1·64	2·30	2·28	3·00	2·76

Several of these, especially that for μ_{C-O}, seem unexpectedly high.

Estimations of induction have also been usefully applied in polarization problems other than the present (cf. *J.C.S.*, 1933, 1551; 1937, 196 and 1992), but they are inevitably somewhat uncertain since, strictly, account should be taken of the intramolecular dielectric constant (which will reduce F_x and F_y), and moreover small errors in r are magnified in the result because distance enters as the third power.

Nevertheless, Smallwood and Herzfeld made obvious one possible mode for the transmission of polarity along a saturated carbon chain (Lapworth's 'imported effect' or Ingold's 'induced effect'): a dipolar radical will polarize an adjacent covalent bond and create therein an induced dipole, which in turn will polarize a third bond, and so on. The magnitudes of these induced moments will fall off in geometrical progression as the number of linkages increases and should be negligible (if the C—C—C chain is an extended zigzag) about three. Thus the pre-1929 indications that the moments of all members of a homologous series were the same could have been forecast as incorrect; later and better measurements demonstrated this to be so, e.g.:

Alkyl-groups	Chlorides*	Bromides*	Iodides*	Cyanides*
CH_3-	$1·87D$	$1·80D$	$1·64D$	$3·94D$
C_2H_5-	$2·05$	$2·01$	$1·87$	$4·04$
$n\text{-}C_3H_7-$	$2·10$	$2·13$	$2·01$	$4·05$
$n\text{-}C_4H_9-$	$2·11$	$2·15$	$2·08$	$4·09$
$n\text{-}C_5H_{11}$	$2·12$	—	—	—

* μ_{gas} as given by Sugden and Groves (*J.C.S.*, 1937, 158).

However, nothing written above will explain the differences in moment commonly observed between simple aliphatic and aromatic derivatives (e.g. the alkyl chlorides with μ *ca.* $2D$ and C_6H_5Cl for which $\mu_{gas}=1·73D$); consideration of such cases forces repudiation of assumption (*a*), basic to vectorial analysis of dipole moments, stated on p. 91. In passing, we may note that the actual value of a 'link moment' (e.g. in the list of Eucken and Meyer) depended upon that for μ_{C-H}, since clearly the resultant for a substance such as chlorobenzene was numerically equal to $\mu_{C-H}+\mu_{C-Cl}$. The fact that toluene had a moment of only *ca.* $0·4$ suggested that this was the upper limit for the C—H link moment, but it also implied that μ_{C-H} in methane might not be the same as μ_{C-H} in benzene; as already hinted, such dissimilarities become clearer when bonds of a higher polarity than C—H were involved.

This problem, with much else encountered during the interpretation of dipole moments, may be qualitatively understood in terms of a theory evolved through the decade 1920–30 to correlate the chemical reactivity of a molecule with the distribution of electric charges within it.

Historically the theory originated from a principle that an octet of electrons is the stable valency shell for the atoms, except hydrogen, commonly entering organic molecules and that, therefore, any electronic deformation of molecules during chemical change is likely to be accomplished with *preservation* of atomic octets. Two obvious mechanisms by which such displacements could occur were early recognized: (1) the *inductive* and (2) the *electromeric* mechanisms.

In the first, the electrical dissymmetry of a dipolar link between two different atoms is considered to be propagated along a chain of atoms by a process analogous to electrostatic induction, the electrons remaining bound in their own atomic octets, a permanent state of polarization resulting. This mechanism was clearly described in 1923 by G. N. Lewis (*Valence and the Structure of Atoms and Molecules*, New York, 1923) and J. J. Thomson (*Phil. Mag.*, 1923, **46**, 407).

In the second, one duplet of a given atomic octet is supposed to be replaced by another. Thus introduction into an octet of an unshared duplet belonging to a neighbouring atom causes ejection of an equivalent duplet which either then becomes unshared or can initiate a similar exchange further along the molecule. This process, due to Lowry (*J.C.S.*, 1923, **123**, 822, 1886; *Nature*, 1925, **114**, 376), represents a transient condition of the molecule, possibly an activation mechanism or polarizability effect.

Organic chemists have used the following conventions to formulate the two mechanisms:

$$CH_3 \longrightarrow CH_2 \longrightarrow Cl \qquad \textit{Inductive effect}$$

$$R_2N\overset{\frown}{\quad} C \overset{\frown}{=\!=} C \overset{\frown}{-} C \overset{\frown}{=\!=} O \qquad \textit{Electromeric effect}$$

The straight arrows indicate the directions towards which the electrons are thought to be concentrated, the curved arrows denote transferable duplets. These correspond to single bonds, so that the second example merely means that the atomic system shown is tending, under some external cause, to assume the state represented by older formulation as the completely dipolar structure: $R_2\overset{\oplus}{N}\!=\!\!C\!-\!C\!=\!\!C\!-\!\overset{\ominus}{O}$.

An important step was taken in 1923–5 by Lucas (*J. Amer. Chem. Soc.*, 1923, **46**, 2475; 1925, **47**, 1459, 1462), who discussed the possibility that the inductive could assist and orient the electromeric mechanism in a molecule. Lowry had simply supposed the polarization of a double bond to be equally possible in both directions:

$R_2C \overset{\frown}{=\!\!=} CX_2$ or $R_2\overset{\frown}{C} =\!\!= CX_2$, Lucas's extension was that the inductive polarization of one link could direct the electromeric polarizability of an adjacent double

bond: thus $CH_3 \rightarrow CH \overset{\frown}{=\!\!=} CH_2$ will occur rather than

$CH_3 \rightarrow \overset{\frown}{CH} =\!\!= CH_2$. In 1926 these ideas were generalized and applied to conjugated systems by Ingold (*J.C.S.*, 1926, 1310) and Robinson (*ibid.*, 1926, 401) with successful results, especially in the field of aromatic substitution.

Ingold plainly envisaged (*Annual Reps.*, 1926, **23**, 129) the possibility of a permanent state of polarization produced by the mechanism of the electromeric effect, in other words, that the *stable* (or *real*) form of a system is possibly *intermediate* between the formally extreme polar structures. Such an effect, like the inductive, should show in the experimentally measurable dipole moment; it is now generally referred to as the *mesomeric* effect.

A physical test for mesomerism was first proposed by Ingold (1926). It consisted of finding a group (—NMe_2 was suggested) such that when linked to an unsaturated system (e.g. a phenyl group) the mesomeric effect opposed and actually outweighed the inductive effect, a result which could be detected by the vector addition method since the direction of the electric moment associated with the saturated aliphatic linking would become apparently reversed in the corresponding aromatic combination.

$$\text{Alphyl} \longrightarrow NR_2 \qquad\qquad \text{Aryl} \longleftarrow NR_2$$

(Dotted arrows show apparent resultant moment directions)

Such tests were later made experimentally by Hojendahl and Sutton (*Proc. Roy. Soc.*, 1931, **133A**, 668). The latter author clearly saw that even when the M effect does not outweigh the I, the differences between the moments of pairs of substances Alphyl-R and Aryl-R, are always in the direction of the mesomerism in the aromatic member. The 'mesomeric moments' associated with various groups were obtained by algebraic subtraction of $\mu_{\text{Alphyl-R}}$ from $\mu_{\text{Aryl-R}}$, these being written $+\mu$ or $-\mu$ if their positive or negative ends respectively were towards the group R:

.I	.Br	.Cl	.CH$_3$	.CN	.CCl$_3$	.NO$_2$
+0·86	+0·69	+0·59	+0·45	−0·43	−0·50	−0·88

Sutton's moments were figures determined in solution, and to allow for induction he compared, whenever possible, C_6H_5-R and Me$_3$C-R. Subsequently Groves and Sugden (*J.C.S.*, 1937, 1992), using μ_{gas} data throughout, in conjunction with their own values of link moments (given above), have attempted to calculate all the secondary induced moments in certain benzene derivatives of the type C_6H_5-R. From the equation: $\mu_{\text{observed}} = \mu_{\text{link}} + \Sigma\mu_{\text{induced}} + \mu_{\text{mesomeric}}$ they thus evaluated the following mesomeric moments:

.F	.Cl.	.Br	.I	.CN	.NO$_2$
+1·00	+0·97	+0·89	+0·87	−0·05	−0·29

These agreed in sign with Sutton's original estimates, but differed in magnitudes and in the arrangement of the halogens. Audsley and Goss (*J.C.S.*, 1942, 497) have confirmed this sequence, recording the mesomerie moments in the phenyl halides as:

.F	.Cl	.Br	.I
+1·04	+0·95	+0·74	+0·51

(incidentally pointing out that $\mu_{\text{mesomeric}} = 1\cdot15 - 0\cdot012Z$, where Z is the atomic number of the halogen), while Baker and Hopkins (*J.C.S.*, 1949, 1089) have shown such an order to be reconcilable with chemical behaviour. Baddeley (*J.C.S.*, 1950, 663) has provided a simple physical picture to explain how these and other atoms X stand relatively in their abilities to release electrons in the direction of their primary bonds C—X; he suggests that mesomeric effects are proportional to the sizes of the ratio $(r^2 + 1\cdot22^2)^{\frac{1}{2}}/r$, where r is the single bond (or X-ray) radius of the atom X. Accordingly the mesomeric moments of F, Cl, Br, and I should be as

$$2\cdot15:1\cdot58:1\cdot44:1\cdot33,$$

i.e. a series resembling those of Sugden and Goss. Considered against the moments to be expected for the fully dipolar forms (10 to 20D units), any of these sets show how small is the actual reversal of polarity taking place in a molecule.

Mesomerism is not tautomerism between extreme structures, such as—in the case of chlorobenzene— A and B.

$\mu \doteq -2D$ $\mu \doteq \underline{ca} + 20D$

This is clear from the observed moments: an unperturbed structure such as A would have a moment not greater than -2 units, B would have roughly the value shown above. A mixture of the two forms would—since the moment enters the orientation polarization as its square —show an apparent moment higher than 2. On the other hand, an intermediate structure, C, in which A has been modified towards B (shown by the curved arrows), will show an apparent moment which is vectorially between the figures given. The observed dipole moment for chlorobenzene is about 1·6. The former hypothesis is untenable unless it is supposed that the tautomeric interchange $A \rightleftharpoons B$ occurs more rapidly than *ca.* 10^{12} per second, i.e. the frequency at which dipolar molecules cease to be able to follow the reversals of the field. Such short-lived tautomerides could scarcely be regarded as being distinct molecular states.

For these reasons, then, the real structure of any substance will always lie between unreal extreme states, which alone can be accurately formulated. Qualitatively the mesomeric form can be indicated by superimposing modifications on these extreme (or unperturbed or canonical) structures (*J.C.S.* 1933, 1120). Many examples of this phenomenon have already been recognized. The following are clear cases where dipole moments afford evidence: *The nitro-group* theoretically could exist

in the two unperturbed forms $-N\!\!\begin{smallmatrix}O\\ \diagdown O\end{smallmatrix}$ and $-N\!\!\begin{smallmatrix}\diagup O\\ O\end{smallmatrix}$,

both of which have considerable resultant moments *not* lying along the bond joining the N atom to carbon, &c. Actually, however, 4:4'-dinitrodiphenyl and 1:4-dinitrobenzene have *ca.* zero moments, from which fact the conclusion has been drawn that the real structure of

the nitro-group has a symmetrical Y-form: $-\overset{\oplus}{N}\!\!\begin{smallmatrix}O\\ \diagup\\ \diagdown\\ O\end{smallmatrix}\!\!\bigg\}\ominus$.

The aliphatic diazo-compounds have the two unperturbed structures $R_2\overset{\oplus}{C}=N\!:\!\overset{\ominus}{N}$ and $R_2\overset{\ominus}{C}-\overset{\oplus}{N}\equiv N$, each of which would possess a moment of some 4 units. The observed value is only $1·42D$, i.e. *vectorially* between the large but oppositely acting moments of the extreme forms. *The organic azides* are a similar instance: $R-N=\overset{\oplus}{N}=\overset{\ominus}{N}$ and

$R—\overset{\ominus}{N}—\overset{\oplus}{N}\equiv N$ should both require $\mu=4D$, but with opposite algebraical signs. The observed figure is $1\cdot55$ units.

With many structures, of course, mesomeric moments may augment the primary moment or moments and cause resultants of a high order; outstanding instances of this occur among the 'endo' compounds of Busch (e.g. the reagent 'nitron', $\mu=7\cdot2D$) or the 'sydnones', whose real forms must be considered as intermediate between a considerable number of strongly polar extreme structures. Formulae for these are too extensive for reproduction here; they may be seen in *J.C.S.*, 1948, 2269; 1949, 746.

An example worth mentioning involves the group ($.NMe_2$) originally suggested by Ingold in 1926 as likely to provide physical evidence for mesomerism (cf. above). The moment observed for dimethylaniline is $1\cdot58D$. An analysis of this figure by Marsden and Sutton (*J.C.S.*, 1936, 599) indicated that $\mu_{mesomeric}$ was *ca.* $1\cdot5D$, although the problem was complicated by the probability that $\mu_{resultant}$ was not collinear with the $C_6H_5—N$ axis, due to the three N-valency directions being themselves non-planar. With various *para*-substituted molecules of type $X.C_6H_4.NR_2$ the occurrence of mesomerism can be seen at once: whatever the orientation of $\mu_{resultant}$ in $C_6H_5.NR_2$, the moment of p-$X.C_6H_4.NR_2$ *without mesomerism* should not exceed the sum ($\mu_{C_6H_5.NR_2}+\mu_{C_6H_5.X}$), yet in fact it does so even when $X=Cl$ (Sutton reporting $\mu_{Cl.C_6H_4.NMe_2}=3\cdot29D$ against $\mu_{C_6H_5.NMe_2}=1\cdot58D$ and $\mu_{C_6H_5.Cl}=1\cdot56D$). The nitroso-group is perhaps most striking. Nitrosobenzene itself had a moment of $3\cdot1D$ while a comparable aliphatic substance showed only $2\cdot5D$ (Sutton *et al.*, *J.C.S.*, 1932, 742); $\mu_{mesomeric}$ in $C_6H_5.NO$ was therefore *ca.* $-0\cdot6D$ (see p. 98). The polarities of p-nitrosodimethyl- and diethyl-anilines, however, are much greater than $3\cdot1 + \mu_{C_6H_5 . NR_2}$ (Le Fèvre and Smith, *J.C.S.*, 1932, 2239):

| $C_6H_5 . NMe_2$ | $1\cdot6D$ | $p\text{-(NO)}.C_6H_4.NMe_2$ | $6\cdot9D$ |
| $C_6H_5NEt_2$ | $1\cdot8D$ | $p\text{-(NO)}.C_6H_4.NEt_2$ | $7\cdot2D$ |

Evidently here the mesomeric effects of $.NR_2$ and $.NO$ are reinforcing one another in the sense:

$$R_2N\overset{\frown}{-}C=\overset{\frown}{C}-C=\overset{\frown}{C}-N=\overset{\frown}{O}.$$

The $.NO$ group is additionally interesting because in certain chemical reactions it presumably polarizes in an opposite manner (see Le Fèvre, *J.C.S.*, 1931, 810).

A mathematical description of mesomerism is possible through the so-called wave function ψ for the most stable state of a system of atoms composing a molecule (cf. Pauling and Wilson, *Introduction to Quantum Mechanics*, McGraw-Hill Book Co., New York, 1935). With knowledge of ψ for a given system, the numerical value of any property capable of measurement is—in theory at least—accessible to calculation; strictly, the setting up of ψ requires solution of the partial differential wave equation of Schrodinger, but since in practice this is complicated approximate methods are therefore used. One of these is to assume that ψ is a linear combination of the wave functions $\psi_1, \psi_2, \psi_3 \ldots$, &c., for the various unperturbed states: $\psi = \alpha_1\psi_1 + \alpha_2\psi_2 + \alpha_3\psi_3 + \ldots$, in which the best relative values of the numerical coefficients α_1, α_2, &c., are such as make the energy corresponding to ψ a minimum.

Sutton (*Trans. Far. Soc.*, 1934, **30,** 789) has outlined the simplest case where one real form has only two unperturbed contributing structures. Here $\psi = \alpha_1\psi_1 + \alpha_2\psi_2$, and $\alpha_1^2 + \alpha_2^2 = 1$. The functions ψ, ψ_1 and ψ_2 may be correlated with the dipole moments of the molecules concerned. If the latter have moments along the x axis given by μ_{1x} and μ_{2x} respectively, then the moment of the real (or hybrid) state along this axis is

$$\mu = \alpha_1^2\mu_{1x} + \alpha_2^2\mu_{2x} + 2\alpha_1\alpha_2 e\int_{-\infty}^{+\infty}\psi_1\left(\sum_{i=1}^{n}x_i - a\right)\psi_2 dr$$

where e is the electronic charge, a is the x co-ordinate of the centroid of positive charge, and the suffix i refers to the ith electron, there being n in all. The integral cannot be exactly evaluated, but in general it will be small so that one can write $\mu = \alpha_1^2\mu_{1x} + \alpha_2^2\mu_{2x}$, and if the experimentally observed μ, μ_{1x} and μ_{2x} are known an idea of the relative contributions of the states can be achieved.

For example, if carbon dioxide is a hybrid of $(+)O\equiv C{-}O(-)$ and $(-)O{-}C\equiv O(+)$, then—since $\mu_{observed} = 0$—evidently $\alpha_1 = \alpha_2$. Similar deductions follow from the near zero moments recorded for certain unsymmetrical molecules (e.g. CO, or NO) derived *inter alia* from ionized forms $(+)A{-}B(-)$ and $(-)A{-}B(+)$, the moments of which would be about equal although opposite in sign. Properly the fully covalent types $A{=}B$ should be considered as well, but because these are likely to have very small polarities (Mulliken, *J. Chem. Phys.*, 1935, **3**, 573) they may be neglected in a rough analysis. Thus the hydrogen halides can be regarded as hybrids of $H.X$, H^+X^-, and H^-X^+; the second of these is (because of the relative electronegativities of H and X) obviously much more stable than the third (which, like the first, may be ignored), so that its importance can be assessed directly from $(\mu_{HX})_{observed}$. Taking HCl as a particular instance: $\mu_{H^+{CL}^-} =$(electronic charge) (interatomic distance)$= 6{\cdot}07D$; $\mu_{observed} = 1{\cdot}08D$, whence $\alpha_2^2 = ca.\ 0{\cdot}18$, in other words, the linkage in hydrogen chloride may crudely be thought as having 18 per cent ionic character. Analogous figures for HF, HBr, and HI are, in order, 44, 11, and 5 per cent. Ionic character usually increases with bond multiplicity, e.g. whenever the $C{-}O$ or $C{=}O$

links are found with apparent moments of 0·7 or 2·3D and with internuclear separations of 1·43 or 1·24 A their ionic characters will be around 10 or 40 per cent respectively. Pauling (*The Nature of the Chemical Bond*, Cornell Univ. Press, 1945, Chap. II) has discussed in this manner many of the bonds occurring in organic chemistry, and may be consulted for further illustrations.

To end this discussion attention should be drawn to procedures of calculation, now under development, directed towards revealing the relative distributions of π-electrons in organic molecules. The π-electrons are those responsible for the mesomeric effect. They are assumed to move in orbits covering the whole molecule, in contradistinction to the σ- electrons which are paired in localized bonds between neighbouring atoms and take no part in bond conjugation. Each of these molecular orbitals ϕ can be represented approximately by a linear combination of n-atomic orbitals, n being the number of atomic centres concerned. Accordingly, ϕ can be written
$$\phi = c_1\psi_1 + c_2\psi_2 + \ldots c_n\psi_n.$$

A completely worked example for acridine is set out by Coulson and Longuet-Higgins (*Trans. Far. Soc.*, 1947, **43**, 87). Ultimately, using the normalization condition that $c_1^2 + c_2^2 + \ldots c_n^2 = 1$ in each orbital, the absolute magnitudes of the coefficients c_1, c_2, &c., are found, and the final density of π-electrons at, say, atom i is then given by $2\Sigma c_i^2$. Results are commonly expressed by structural formulae carrying numbers at each atom denoting the total mobile charge carried there. Theoretically from these π-electron distributions, mesomeric molecular moments should be calculable, which, when compounded with the vector sum of the relevant σ-bond moments (i.e. μ_{HC}, 0·4; μ_{HN}, 1·3; μ_{CN}, 0·45; μ_{CO}, 0·8; μ_{NO}, 0·5; all in the sense μ_{+-}) should produce resultants approaching the experimentally observed values.

To date, success has been limited. Several authors

have addressed themselves to pyridine for which moments varying from 1·48 to 4·93D have been forecast (the moment found is about 2·2 units). Details are contained in the following papers: Coulson *et al.*, *J.C.S.*, 1949, 971, 1983; Pullman *et al.*, *Bull. Soc. chim.*, 1950, 34; Ploquin, *ibid.*, 1948, 640, *Compt. rend.*, 1948, **226**, 245, 339; Sutton *et al.*, *Trans. Far. Soc.*, 1951, **47**, 113, *J.C.S.*, 1951, 2821.

Absolute Determination of Bond Polarity. Enough has already been mentioned to suggest that a bond moment is *not* a constant quantity from molecule to molecule, and that even its value in a given molecule cannot usually be deduced with certainty by vectorial analysis of the measured $\mu_{resultant}$. Obvious exceptions to the last statement are, of course, diatomic molecules, and a few other simple structures for which intervalency angles (θ) are known accurately; thus the bond moments in the molecules named may be accepted as 'directly' determined:

HF	1·91D	O—H (in H_2O, $\mu=1·84$, $\theta=105°$)	1·50D
HCl	1·08D	S—H (in H_2S, $\mu=0·89$, $\theta=92°$)	0·64D
HBr	0·79D	NO (in nitric oxide)	0·16D
HI	0·38D	CO (in carbon monoxide)	0·12D

If a bond between two atoms is regarded as a resonance hybrid of various states, then vectorial treatment is permissible only if the weights of these states remain the same for all situations of the bond concerned. Sometimes this condition is evidently roughly satisfied, as in the examples quoted on p. 90; an extreme instance where it is not is provided by $\mu_{carbon\ monoxide}=0·12D$, from which vectorially one cannot compute the moments of CH_2O (2·27D), Me_2CO (about 2·9D), $CH_2{:}CO$ (1·52D), &c.

However, in principle, two routes exist whereby an actual bond moment may be estimated. They have been indicated previously (pp. 20 and 24). Both involve data

8

derived from infra-red spectroscopy. Neither seems yet capable of high experimental accuracy.

The first requires knowledge of the atomic polarization of a symmetrical molecule, e.g. CX_4, together with the bending force constant for deformation of the X—C—X valency angle. By the argument on pp. 23 and 24, μ_{C-X} then follows straightforwardly. Thus taking for methane Watson's observed $_AP$ of 0·08 c.c. in conjunction with an H—C—H force constant of $5·7 \times 10^{-12}$ erg/radian gives $\mu_{CH} = \pm 0·35D$. The poor precision with which $_AP$ can be measured is a weakness, e.g. using the 2·4 c.c. listed for CCl_4 on p. 19, together with $V_1 = 1·02 \times 10^{-11}$ (cf. Herzberg, *Infra-red and Raman Spectra*, van Nostrand, New York, 1945, p. 182), leads to $\mu_{CCl} = \pm 2·7D$, while the lower $_AP$ (viz. 1·2 c.c.) reported by Cartwright and Errera (p. 20) corresponds to $\mu_{CCl} = \pm 1·9D$. The latter figure seems more reasonable. In the same way, from Sutton's recorded $_AP$'s for $GeCl_4$, $TiCl_4$, and $SnCl_4$, the moments of the Ge—Cl, Ti—Cl, and Sn—Cl bonds respectively emerge as $\pm 3·2$, $\pm 2·2$, and $\pm 3·5D$ (appropriate force constants are listed by Herzberg). Such values are not unlikely when considered against the few available relevant results in the literature, e.g. the molecular moments of Et_3SnCl ($3·4D$, in CCl_4), Et_3SiCl ($2·1D$, in CCl_4), Ph_3GeBr ($2·35D$, in C_6H_6), &c. Likewise, if carbon dioxide is regarded as two independent one-dimensional oscillators, then with $V_1 = 0·74 \times 10^{-11}$, μ_{CO} appears (from $_AP = 0·81$ or 0·75 c.c.) to be $\pm 1·8D$, i.e. *ca.* the mean of μ_{C-O} and $\mu_{C=O}$.

The second method basically requires measurements of the *intensities* of selected absorption bands in the infra-red spectrum of a substance. The mathematical theory is set out in Herzberg's book (p. 261), quoted a few lines above, while the techniques to be adopted may be studied in the papers cited on p. 20, together with others mentioned below. In essence, if a is the absorption co-efficient, the radiation transmitted through a cell of length l containing a gas at pressure p is given by $I = I_0 \exp(-apl)$, where I_0 refers to the incident beam. I, I_0, and a are functions of the frequency v. For a given absorption band the absolute intensity of absorption A_i follows as the area beneath the corresponding $a \times v$ curve. Absorption is due to changes in the dipole moment μ of the vibrating molecule when its atoms are displaced from their equilibrium positions by valence stretching and bending motions. The various links in a molecule, in each making these vibrations, cause specific bands in the spectrum, thus allowing the assignment (or connection) of a given absorption frequency to a particular interatomic vibration (cf. Thompson, *J.C.S.*, 1948, 328). The A_i figures for these recognized stretching or bending motions depend respectively on $(\partial \mu_{bond} / \partial r)^2$ or $(\mu_{bond})^2$, r being the length of the bond in question. Important assumptions made are that $\partial \mu_{bond}$ is a linear function of ∂r for the first mode, or—for the second—that the moment of a bond is unaltered during deflection.

So far, applications of this method have been mostly to the C—H link in hydrocarbons and to the few cases of CO, CS, and NO bonds occurring in small molecules such as CO_2, OCS or N_2O. The trend of current development may be inferred from the papers, e.g. of Robinson (*J. Chem. Physics*, 1951, **19**, 881), Francis (*ibid.*, 942), Cole and Thompson (*Trans. Far. Soc.*, 1950, **46**, 103), and Crawford and Dinsmore (*J. Chem. Physics*, 1950, **18**, 983, 1682).

Some examples of the polarities obtained are given in the following table, bending vibrations being used throughout (in the aromatic cases, the 'out-of-plane' motions). The trio of values against C_2H_4 and C_2H_6 are the results for different bending modes. To these may be added Thorndike's estimate of $\pm 1 \cdot 17 D$ for μ_{CO} in carbon dioxide.

Molecules	$\pm \mu_{CH}(D)$	Authors
Methane	0·307	Rollefson and Havens (1)
Ethylene	0·77	Thorndike et al., 1947
	0·52	
	0·37	
Ethane	0·104	Thorndike, 1947
	0·35	
	0·30	
Hydrogen cyanide	0·57	Foley (2)
Chloroform	0·3	Timm and Mecke (3)
Benzene and 35 substituted derivatives	Mean value = 0·57	Thompson et al. (4) and 1950

(1) *Physical Rev.*, 1940, **57**, 710; (2) *Physical Rev.*, 1946, **69**, 628; (3) *Z. physikal. Chem.*, 1935, **98**, 363; (4) *Proc. Roy. Soc.*, 1948, **192A**, 492. References shown as years are given in the text.

Typical of the $\pm(\partial\mu/\partial r)$ ratios recorded are: 0·55 (CH$_4$), 0·75 (C$_2$H$_6$) or 0·63 (C$_2$H$_4$); they have the dimensions of a charge and may be compared with that of an electron $4\cdot80 \times 10^{-10}$ c.g.s. units. In general, $\partial\mu/\partial r$ is greater than $\mu_{bending}/$(equilibrium inter-nuclear distance), suggesting a non-simple relationship between μ and r.

The tabulated figures are of the orders of those computable from atomic polarizations. They may be interpreted as showing the effects of environment on the C—H moment. Actually, since the quantity determined is μ^2 or $(\partial\mu/\partial r)^2$, the sign of μ_{CH} is unknown and the range of variation thereby increased.

The problem of the correct value of μ_{CH} underlay the earlier attempts to deduce bond moments (cf. p. 95). Smyth (*J. Physical Chem.*, 1937, **41**, 209), reviewing the then extant data, concluded that the polarity was $(\delta-)$C—H$(\delta+)$ and in magnitude $0\cdot4D$. In 1942, however, Coulson (*Trans. Far. Soc.*, 1942, **38**, 433) argued theoretically that in methane the C—H links have a contrary polarization, viz. $(\delta+)C—H(\delta-)$. Walsh (in *J.C.S.*, 1948, 398, and other papers) has extended this idea and correlated *inter alia* intermolecular distance, hybrid composition, and polarity:

Molecule	C valency towards H	$r_{C-H}A$	Polarity
CH radical	p	1·131	$(\delta+)C—H(\delta-)$
CH_4	sp^3	1·094	
C_2H_4	sp^2	1·071	$\downarrow$
C_2H_2	sp	1·059	$(\delta-)C—H(\delta+)$

The reversal is thought to occur between CH_4 and C_2H_4, and benzene, with r_{CH} 1·04–1·08A, to have the polarities disposed as $(\delta-)C—H(\delta+)$.

If the C—H bonds in methyl are polarized in the sense of those in methane, then the observed moment of toluene should act as though directed $(\delta+)C_6H_5Me(\delta-)$. Yet vectorial indications (cf. p. 89) are that the Me— group is positive with respect to the ring. One suggestion (Smyth, *J. Amer. Chem. Soc.*, 1943, **65**, 89) to resolve the difficulty is that structures such as $(-)C_6H_5 . CH_2H(+)$ contribute to the real form. This is hyperconjugation (or 'no-bond resonance'), which, on the figures tabulated above, will need to cause a moment of $+1·2$ to $+1·3D$ to allow the observed moment to be $+0·4D$. (See 'Polarity of the C—H Bond', Gent, *Quarterly Revs.*, 1948, **2**, 382.)

SOME SIMPLE APPLICATIONS OF DIPOLE MOMENTS IN CHEMISTRY

Undoubtedly the most successful applications of dipole moments to the solution of structural problems have occurred where an exact quantitative analysis of results has not been necessary, e.g. in questions involving a choice of configurations, where the possible isomerides should have widely differing moments. A number of such cases, additional to those of ethylene and benzene which have already been discussed, are included below:

(1) *The Diphenyl Compounds*. The 4:4′-dihalogeno-derivatives were found to possess zero moments. Structures based on the formula of Kaufler and requiring large μ's were, therefore, obviously incorrect and were properly replaced by extended linear formulae.

(2) *Azo-, Azoxy-, and Diazo-compounds*. Azobenzene exists in two forms of m.p. 68·0° or 71·4°. Since their moments, found in benzene solution, are *ca.* 0 or 3·0*D* respectively, the lower melting isomer is identifiable as the *trans* and the higher as the *cis* modification of $C_6H_5.N:N.C_6H_5$ (Hartley and Le Fèvre, *J.C.S.*, 1939, 531). Both varieties when dissolved and exposed to sunlight suffer interconversion, the same equilibrium mixture being produced from either starting material. The apparent moment of the 'equilibrated' azobenzene (in benzene) is 1·4*D*, indicating a *cis*-content of about 22 per cent. The two azoxybenzenes, $C_6H_5.N:NO.C_6H_5$, with m.p.s of 36° and 84°, and showing moments of 1·7 and 4·7*D*, are analogous examples.

Le Fèvre *et al.* (*J.C.S.*, 1938, 431; 1949, 333; 1950, 3128) have recorded the moments of a number of isomeric pairs of the aromatic diazocyanides:

Diazocyanide	$\mu_{\text{labile form}}$	$\mu_{\text{stable form}}$
α-Naphthalene-	3·2*D*	5·6*D*
β-Naphthalene-	4·0	6·9
Diphenyl-4-	4·5	5·5
4-Chlorobenzene-	2·9	3·7
4-Bromobenzene-	2·9	3·8
4-Nitrobenzene-	2·0	1·5
2:4:6-Tribromobenzene-	2·5	4·0

The absence of a constant difference between the values for each pair shows that they cannot be *trans*- individuals related as nitrile and *iso*nitrile (Orton, 1905). A detailed analysis supports Hantzsch's original (1894) hypothesis of geometrical isomerism in the following manner:

$$X.C_6H_4.N \quad\quad\quad X.C_6H_4.N$$
$$\parallel \quad\quad\quad\quad\quad\quad \parallel$$
$$(CN).N \quad\quad\quad\quad N.(CN)$$

Labile forms   Stable forms

Incidentally, it is worth mentioning that the dielectric constant is a convenient property with which to measure photo- or thermochemical interconversion rates of many of these substances in solution (see *J.C.S.*, 1949, 944).

(3) *Carbon Suboxide and Diiodoacetylene.* Since zero moments have been reported for both these substances (*J.C.S.*, 1933, 652; 1935, 1696), the cyclic representation of Boersch for the former and the unsymmetrical structure ($C:CI_2$) of Nef for the latter can be discarded in favour of the simpler rectilinear formulae.

(4) *Oximes and Anils.* The investigations of Meisenheimer and Brady indicated that the configurations of oximes given by Hantzsch and Werner should be interchanged. Physical evidence in support of this proposal was found by Taylor and Sutton (*J.C.S.*, 1931, 2190; 1933, 63) as follows: The N-methyl ethers of 4-nitrobenzophenoneoxime were found to have moments of $6.6D$ and $1.09D$. In the former, obviously the components $\mu_{C \to NO_2}$, and $\mu_{N \to O}$ must be acting in the same sense.

Accordingly the true configurations must be:

$$\text{(A)} \quad O \leftarrow NCH_3 \quad\quad\quad CH_3N \to O \quad \text{(B)}$$
$$\mu = 6.6\,D \quad\quad\quad\quad \mu = 1.09\,D$$

But the ether with the higher moment was obtained

from that oxime which gave *p*-nitrobenzanilide by the Beckmann change, i.e.

(A) NO_2—⬡—CPh →(Beckmann Change)→ NO_2—⬡—C:O
        ‖ |
      HO·N   Ph·NH

Thus an independent physical proof was provided that the Beckmann change involves a *trans* interchange of groups.

De Gaouck and Le Fèvre (*J.C.S.*, 1938, 741) have investigated the possible existence of geometrically isomeric forms of anils (R—CH=N—R'). However, corresponding to a given formula, only *one* anil is found. The moments of C_6H_5—CH=N—C_6H_5 and

$$4:4'\text{-Cl}—C_6H_4—CH=N—C_6H_4—Cl$$

are equal within the limits of experimental error ($1\cdot56-1\cdot57D$). It is therefore evident that the dichloro-derivative has a *trans* structure with the two C—Cl links approximately parallel. It is probable that throughout the whole series the *trans* form is so much the more stable that it alone occurs.

(5) *Cyclohexane Derivatives and Other Pliable Ring Compounds.* The observed moment $1\cdot3D$ (Le Fèvre and Le Fèvre, *J.C.S.*, 1935, 1696) of cyclohexa-1:4-dione corresponds to a *cis:trans* equilibrium of *ca.* 20:80, respectively. This result provides physical evidence for the existence of the Sachse-Mohr type of non-planar strainless rings. Hassel (*Chem. Zentr.*, 1930, 1956, cf. *Acta chem. scand.*, 1947, **1**, 683) has shown that the α- and β-benzene hexachlorides ($C_6H_6Cl_6$) have moments of $2\cdot2$ and $0D$ units, respectively. The latter form, therefore, almost certainly possesses the (*trans*) 'chair', rather than the pliable 'boat', configuration.

The skeleton of 1:4-dioxan may be flexible, like *cyclo*-hexadione, although the polarization-temperature relationship for this substance as a gas indicates non-polarity. Measurements in benzene leave open the possibility of a small moment.

Two naphthadioxans are known, however, whose structures are such that $cis \rightleftharpoons trans$ conversions of the separate rings are prevented. The dipole moments of these two forms are distinctive: cis, $\mu = 1.90$; $trans$,

1:4-Dioxan cis- and $trans$-Naphthadioxans

$\mu = 0.72D$, and give clear evidence that in the former compound the two six rings are coupled in the cis relationship.

The moment of 1:4-dithian resembles that of its oxygen analogue in being $ca.$ $0D$. For trioxymethylene and trithioformaldehyde Calderbank and Le Fèvre have found $\mu = 2.2$ and $2.4D$, respectively, and interpreted these as due to a predominance of 'chair' forms ($J.C.S.$, 1949, 199).

An interesting fact is that thianthren has the appreciable polarity of 1.5 units—a datum implying a non-planar configuration. Bennett and Glasstone ($J.C.S.$, 1934, 128) considered the molecule to be folded about the S—S line, and as a consequence to possess C—S—C angles of less than 120°. Measurements ($J.C.S.$, 1938, 404) on the analogous selanthren show that similar conclusions may be drawn for divalent Se atoms. Phenazine has a moment indistinguishable from zero and is therefore presumably rigidly flat, in contrast to the S and Se compounds. This is explicable if phenazine is mesomeric between a number of unqerturbed structures, such as that indicated, each of which is itself planar. The analogous mechanism would be operative in thianthren and selanthren to a much less extent, so that flexibility need not be seriously inhibited.

Thianthren forms two disulphoxides, m.p. 249° and

Thianthren   Phenazine

284°, with dipole moments of 4·2 and 1·7D, respectively; these substances illustrate the caution which is necessary when interpreting such measurements. At first glance they would be identified as the *cis* and *trans* modifications, respectively (considered in respect of the dispositions of the O-atoms above and below the hetero-cyclic ring). Yet, because of the folded configuration of thianthren itself, the situation is complicated, and deeper consideration assigns the lower moment to the *cis*-form and the higher to the *trans*- (cf. Taylor, *J.C.S.*, 1935, 625).

(6) *Naphthalene Derivatives*. A planar structure for the carbon skeleton of naphthalene is suggested by the non-polarity of 2:6-dichloronaphthalene, for if the molecule were folded about the bond common to both rings any 2:6-disubstituted naphthalene would have a finite resultant moment.

(7) *Tetranitromethane*. Suggestions to the effect that the constitution of this substance is $(NO_2)_3C \cdot O \cdot N:O$ (i.e. a nitrite) cannot be correct since it is completely non-polar. Its formula is, therefore, $C(NO_2)_4$ with the four C—N links symmetrically disposed about the central carbon atom.

(8) *Hexamethylenetetramine*. Various formulae have

been proposed for this relatively complex molecule. Some of these would give rise to a resultant moment. However, Le Fèvre and Rayner (*J.C.S.*, 1938, 1921) found that this substance in chloroform solution has a total polarization practically equal to the observed

molecular refraction. It is, therefore, non-polar. The usually accepted formulation—that of Duden and Scharff (annexed formula)—has a centre of symmetry when erected in three dimensions and thus corresponds to a non-polar molecule. X-ray and electron diffraction data relating to the solid and vapour states, respectively, also allow this structure.

(9) *Glucose*. The moments of α- and β-pentaacetyl-glucoses are 3·5 and 2·5D units, respectively. It is, therefore, obvious that the β is a less unsymmetrical form than the α. This supports the conclusion reached from chemical evidence that in β-glucose the hydrogen atoms attached to carbon atoms Nos. 1 to 5 are arranged alternately above and below the plane of the pyranose ring, whilst in α-glucose the configuration of the first carbon atom is inverted.

On the whole, dipole moments have been little used in the carbohydrate field. The difficulties are illustrated, for example, in the paper by Angyal and Angyal on the polarities of Cyclitol acetates (*J.C.S.*, 1952, 695).

(10) *Configurations of Inorganic Compounds*. The non-polarity found for a number of simpler metallic derivatives, e.g. $Ni(CO)_4$, $SnCl_4$, $TiCl_4$, &c., is a definite indication that their molecules are centrosymmetric.

The main applications of dipole moments have been to 'complex compounds' in cases where a problem of configuration allotment exists. Thus Sugden and Cavell (*J.C.S.*, 1935, 621) used the moments of various nickel glyoximes to support the view that these compounds are planar and that the higher melting forms have the *trans*-configuration. Buraway and Gibson (*J.C.S.*, 1935, 219) found that diethylmonobromogold had no moment, in agreement with the following general bimolecular

formula

$$R\diagdown_{R}\diagup^{Br}\diagdown_{Br}\diagup^{R}_{R}$$

proposed for such dialkyl compounds. Mono-*n*-propyldibromogold by contrast, like triethylstannic-chloride ($3 \cdot 44D$) and diethylstannic dichloride ($3 \cdot 85D$), had a considerable moment (probably between 5 and 6D units).

Mann and Purdie (*J.C.S.*, 1936, 873), having isolated various dichlorobis(trialkylphosphine)-μ-dichlorodipalladiums and the corresponding arsines, attempted to decide which of the three possible formulae, A, B, or C, is correct.

$$R_3P\diagdown_{R_3P}\diagup Pd \diagup^{Cl}\diagdown_{Cl} Pd \diagup^{Cl}_{Cl} \quad A$$

$$R_3P\diagdown_{Cl}\diagup Pd \diagup^{Cl}\diagdown_{Cl} Pd \diagup^{PR_3}_{Cl} \quad B$$

$$R_3P\diagdown_{Cl}\diagup Pd \diagup^{Cl}\diagdown_{Cl} Pd \diagup^{Cl}_{PR_3} \quad C$$

The moments of the tri-*n*-butylphosphine and arsine derivatives, respectively, were $2 \cdot 34$ and $2 \cdot 52D$. Noting that $(Et_3P)_2PdCl_2$ and $(Et_3As)_2PdCl_2$, which are both *trans*, have $\mu = 1 \cdot 05$ and $1 \cdot 04D$, while the *trans* and *cis* forms of dichlorobisdiethylsulphideplatinum differ in

moment by *ca.* $7D$ units, Mann and Purdie expected
A, B, and C to possess moments roughtly 12–14, 7–8,
and 0–1D. The experimental results thus indicate the

$$Et_3S \diagdown Pt \diagup Cl \qquad Et_2S \diagdown Pt \diagup Cl$$

$$\mu = 2\cdot41 \qquad\qquad \mu = 9\cdot5$$

trans symmetrical structure (type C) as the most probable, although the possibility of an equilibrium between
B and C is not excluded. Further examples, relating to
platinous compounds of the form PtA_2X_2, are listed by
Mellor (*Chemical Revs.*, 1943, **33**, 137).

It should be remembered (cf. p. 25) that these large
complex metal-containing molecules may have abnorm-
ally high atomic polarizations, or show marked 'solvent
effects'. Either cause will lead to false values of the
molecular moment. With such compounds, therefore,
the method must be applied with caution.

(11) *Moments of Inorganic Salts.* Wrede (*Z. Physik,*
1927, **44**, 261), using the molecular beam method, found
$\mu = ca.$ 10D units for various alkali halides. This figure is
of the order to be expected if in the process of salt
formation an electron had been transferred through a
distance of about 2 Å, i.e. if the link holding kation to
anion were completely polar. Only a few measurements
have been made in solution, owing chiefly to the sparing
solubility of most salts in the usual non-polar solvents.
Malone and Ferguson (*J. Chem. Physics*, 1934, **2**, 99)
have found 7·84 for lithium perchlorate in dioxan,
whilst Kraus and Hooper (*J. Amer. Chem. Soc.*, 1934,
56, 2265), repeating an earlier determination of Williams
on silver perchlorate in benzene, record a limiting molecular polarization of the order 2,000 c.c., corresponding
to a moment of the expected magnitude. Le Fèvre and
Le Fèvre (*J.C.S.*, 1936, 398) have made minimum

estimates of the dipole moments of two oxonium salts (2-phenyl- and 2-phenyl-3-methylbenzopyrylium perchlorates) in dimethylaniline solution. The results, 8 and 7D units, respectively, fully support the current conception of the structures of these substances.

The examples in the preceding eleven paragraphs are representative of many in the literature where dipole moments have provided an immediate solution to a structural problem. Some notes will now be given of instances in which the implications of polarity are of a more general type.

THE PROBLEM OF INTRA-MOLECULAR ROTATION

Theoretically the electronic composition of a C—C single bond offers little resistance to the mutual rotation of the two atoms about the axis joining their centres (cf. papers in the *Far. Soc. Discussion* on 'Hydrocarbons', No. 10, 1951). In reality, of course, to these carbons there are always other atoms attached by links which may be polar. Accordingly volume (steric hindrance) and electrostatic interactions will vary during one complete rotation, i.e. the molecular potential energy plotted against the angle of internal rotation will show maxima and minima; for example, with ethane the former are to be expected at angles of $2\pi/3$, $4\pi/3$, and 2π, and the latter at $\pi/3$, π, $5\pi/3$. When the rotatable parts of a molecule have resultant dipole moments which are not colinear with the axis of rotation, these maxima or minima will differ among themselves, and a series of *instantaneously made* dielectric polarization measurements should produce values of the molecular resultant moment all lying between two extremes and tending towards those appropriate for the configurations of lowest potential energy. The datum observed by normal experiment is therefore a weighted average drawn over a relatively considerable period of time; clearly, also, the precise magnitude of this mean is likely to be affected by the *temperature*, because upon temperature depends the number and violence of the intermolecular collisions by which the shape of a flexible structure might be altered.

In the light of these remarks it is clear that no certain allocation of configuration can be made by vectorial analysis in cases such as the diethyl esters of fumaric and maleic acids, which have moments of $2\cdot4$ and $2\cdot5$–$2\cdot6D$, respectively. Each carbethoxy radical contains within itself the $C\!=\!O$ and $Et\!-\!O$ groups fixed mutually with their moments approximately antiparallel, so that the group resultant moment of $-CO_2R$ does not act along the $C\!-\!(CO_2R)$ link but at some angle to it. Without more information regarding the rotatability of the carbethoxy groups, therefore, the *molecular* resultants of the esters named cannot be predicted. Nevertheless, the *cis* isomer actually has the slightly greater moment; the same is true for the dimethyl *o*- and *p*-phthalates ($\mu = 2\cdot3$–$2\cdot8$ and $2\cdot2D$, respectively) and more definitely so for the three phthalaldehydes (*ortho*-, $4\cdot5$; *meta*-, $2\cdot9$; *para*-, $2\cdot4D$). Yet, on the other hand, the moments of catechol and quinol dimethyl ethers ($1\cdot3$ and $1\cdot8D$) run in the reverse sense.

Clear evidence of restricted rotation about a $C\!-\!C$ bond is found with certain optically active compounds. When these contain only one asymmetric carbon atom the moments of the *d*- or *l*- form separately equals that of the *dl*- isomeride. An interesting situation arises, however, when a molecule incorporates two or more such atoms, because among the inactive varieties will occur *meso*-forms, whose lack of action on polarized light is due to internal compensation (one-half of the molecule is the mirror-image of the other). If models are constructed of the optically active and *meso*-isomerides corresponding to a compound $R_1R_2R_3C\!-\!CR_1R_2R_3$, it will be seen that *only in the meso-form* can the identical substituents simultaneously occupy *trans*-positions. In the optical antipodes this is impossible, and if one pair is placed *trans*, then those remaining become *cis*. If rotation were quite free the moments of the active and *meso*- forms would be the same. In fact they are noticeably different:

Substance	Active	meso-
Stilbene dichloride	2·75D	1·27D
Hydrobenzoin	2·67	2·05
Dimethyl dimethylsuccinate	2·26	2·25
Dimethyl diethylsuccinate	2·27	2·00
Dimethyl dichlorosuccinate	3·03	2·35
Dimethyl dimethoxysuccinate	3·13	2·83
Diethyl dimethoxysuccinate	3·74	3·34
Dimethyl tartrate	2·93	too insol. in C_6H_6

From such figures we may infer that internal rotation is hindered, and that where the *meso*-forms show the smaller moments the *trans* configurations are preferred.

Historically the first *a priori* approach to the general

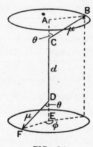

FIG. 24

problem was made by Williams (*Z. physikal Chem.*, 1928, **138**, 75), who calculated the effective resultant moment of two equivalent doublets, μ, rotating *freely* at points d apart and at inclinations $\theta°$ to this vertical direction (see Fig. 24). If one doublet is fixed while the other is allowed to take up all possible positions, given by the angle ϕ, relative to it, only the components AB and EF will contribute to the resultant (since AC and DE being both $\mu \cos \theta$ and situated at $180°$ to one another will cancel vectorially). AB and EF equal $\mu \sin \theta$ and hence μ', the resultant moment of any one configuration, calculated by the usual vector formula, is:

$$\mu' = (2\mu^2 \sin^2 \theta[1 + \cos \phi])^{\frac{1}{2}}; \text{ but } \cos \phi = 2 \cos{}^2 \phi/2 - 1.$$

$$\therefore \ \mu' = 2\mu \sin \theta \cos \phi/2.$$

Experiment actually measures $(\mu')^2$ (in the orientation polarization term). The calculated square of the mean moment is, therefore, given by the integral:

$$\bar{\mu}^2 = \frac{1}{2\pi} \int_0^{2\pi} (2\mu \sin \theta \cos \phi/2)^2 \, d\phi = 2\mu^2 \sin^2 \theta$$

or

$$\bar{\mu} = \sqrt{2} . \mu \sin \theta.$$

The more general case in which the two moments, μ, rotate about axes inclined at an angle α can be dealt with similarly. Thus in Fig. 25, m_1 and m_2 being $\mu \sin \theta$ and

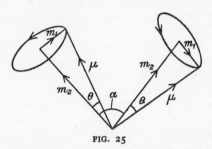

FIG. 25

$\mu \cos \theta$, respectively, the *observed* resultant moment is given by: $\mu_{\text{resultant}} = (2m_1^2 + 4m_2^2 \cos^2 \alpha/2)^{\frac{1}{2}}$. It is seen that if $\alpha = 180°$—the condition represented in Fig. 24— $\mu_{\text{resultant}} = \sqrt{2m_1^2} = \sqrt{2} . \mu \sin \theta$.

These expressions, containing no temperature terms, are applicable only to those, probably non-existent, molecules in which a free rotation of groups can occur;

9

in reality, as already indicated, such movement is likely to be more or less restricted. So far as the relative orientations of two dipoles are concerned, a structure in which these are mutually *trans* is that (out of the infinitude possible) of least potential energy. Since this is also a form for which the molecular resultant is zero, it follows (1) that when internal rotation is hindered, the observed dipole moment should be less than that calculated for free

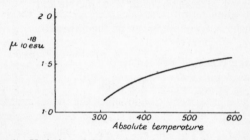

FIG. 26.—Variation of Dipole Moment of Ethylene dichloride with Temperature from measurements made in the gaseous state

rotation and (2) that the effect of a temperature rise should be—by increasing intra-molecular rotation and so diminishing the *trans* content—to produce a higher value for the apparent resultant moment. The realization of both these predictions in practice is illustrated by Fig. 26 for ethylene dichloride, the moment of which for free rotation would be of the order $2 \cdot 4D$.

Meyer (*Z. physikal. Chem.*, 1930, **8B**, 27), taking account of the mutual potential energy of the two moments, has calculated the apparent orientation polarization of a molecule in which such hindered rotation occurs by the methods of classical mechanics, the results being expressed:

$$_0P = \frac{4\pi N}{3}\left[\frac{2\mu^2 \sin^2 \theta}{3kT}(1-x)\right],$$

where x is given by the series development:

$$x = \frac{(\alpha/kT + \beta/(kT)^2 + \gamma/(kT)^3 + \ldots}{(m + n/kT + o/(kT)^2 + p/(kT)^3 \ldots}$$

and α, β, γ, m, n, o, and p are simple functions of factors determining the mutual potential of the doublets and depend on the structure of the molecule. It is obvious that x will diminish with increase of temperature; if the latter is high enough x will be negligible and

$$_0P = \frac{4\pi N}{3}\left[\frac{2\mu^2 \sin^2 \theta}{3kT}\right],$$

i.e. the observed moment will be $\sqrt{2}.\mu \sin \theta$, a result identical with that of Williams. Further, for several substances it has been found that $_0P$ is only seriously reduced when the potential energy is of the order kT, for values $\frac{1}{10}kT$ x is vanishingly small. Since the order of the potential energy, due to the electrostatic repulsions between two dipoles, is given by $\mu_1\mu_2/(\text{distance})^3$, the likelihood of free rotation occurring in a given molecule can possibly be assessed by evaluating $\mu_1\mu_2/kTd^3$. Free rotation might occur when this is less than unity—a condition which is set by the values of the variables:—if the moments are *ca.* $1D$ each, then d must be slightly smaller than 3 Å, if $\mu_1=\mu_2=2D$ units, then the separation must be between 4 and 5 Å, while if $\mu_1=\mu_2=3D$ the corresponding distance must be greater than 6 Å.

The cases of the quinol alkyl ethers (I) and *p*-xylylene dichloride (II) are examples of molecules containing two

(I)   (II)

rotatable doublets separated by distances of the order 6 Å. Using the link moments of Eucken and Meyer, the moment of the methoxyl group can be computed from the values for three C—H links, $0.4D$ each, interacting tetrahedrally plus $0.7D$ for one C—O bond, i.e. as $1.1D$ acting at $110°$ to the bond between the oxygen and the benzene carbon atoms. The resultant moment of the molecule, assuming free rotation, is $\sqrt{2} \cdot \mu \sin\theta = 1.5D$. Recorded observations—all made in solution—lie about $1.7D$; it is notable that for the related case of $4:4'$—dimethoxydiphenyl, in which d is nearly double what it is in (I), a moment of $1.52D$—i.e. very close to the calculated value—has been reported. Similarly, with compound (II) the magnitude and direction of action of the moment of each —CH_2Cl group must first be ascertained; if the usual tetrahedral angles are adopted in conjunction with the just quoted C—H link moment and one of $1.5D$ for the C—Cl bond the required data are respectively $1.8D$ at an angle θ of approximately $80°$. These figures correspond to a resultant moment of 2.4–$2.5D$, in fair agreement with 2.2–$2.3D$ found in benzene solution at $25°$.

It must be admitted, however, that even with the last two instances there is no direct evidence that any *rotation* actually occurs. Especially with the dimethoxy-derivative, there seems a likelihood that mesomerism (through shifts such as Me—Ö—C꞊Ĉ—C, &c.) would *tend* to stabilize the methoxy-groups in the plane of the Ar-ring, and the fact that $\mu_{observed}$ happens to be near that computed for 'free rotation' may be coincidental. This indeed seems to be so with benzil, a single skew configuration for which agrees both with polarity and X-ray data (Caldwell and Le Fèvre, *J.C.S.*, 1939, 1614). The various phenomena recognized as 'steric inhibitions of resonance' (cf. Kadesch and Weller, *J. Amer. Chem. Soc.*,

1941, **63**, 1310; Birtles and Hampson, *J.C.S.*, 1937, 10; Ingham and Hampson, *ibid.*, 1939, 981; and Le Fèvre and Le Fèvre, *ibid.*, 1950, 1829) are relevant also in this connection (e.g. the *reduction* by 0·2D units of polarity of the moment of acetophenone by 2:4:6-trimethyl-substitution is attributed to the volumes of the Me— groups opposing the achievement of the *cis* or *trans* planar structures required by the process C=C—C=O).

Accordingly, for nearly all compounds in which the rotation of polar groups can, in theory, take place, two possibilities may be stated: (1) that there are a pair or more of stable isomers with potential barriers between them high enough to ensure that there are few molecules in intermediate configurations but not so great as to allow the separation of isomers, or (2) that all the molecules have a single type of configuration in each case but that these are in a state of vibration about the form of least energy. These alternatives have been discussed by Bloom and Sutton (*J.C.S.*, 1941, 724), who find a slight balance of evidence for the second view although there is much that is equivocal.

1:2-Dichloroethane is a simple case which has been much examined practically and theoretically. Neither the treatment of Meyer, to which reference has been made, nor the parabolic relation between the polarization and the reciprocal of the absolute temperature which Green and Williams (*Physical Rev.*, 1932, **42**, 119) have derived from it, gives any information concerning the *natures* of the forces determining the configuration of such a molecule.

Regarding these, Smyth, Dornte and Wilson (*J. Amer. Chem. Soc.*, 1931, **53**, 4242) have explored the assumption that they are electrostatic, arising from the repulsions and attractions which can occur between two dipoles in their various mutual orientations. For the potential energy they take $U = \mu_1 \mu_2 (\cos \chi - 3 \cos \alpha_1 \cos$

$\alpha_2)/d^3$, where μ_1 and μ_2 are the two moments, d is the distance between them, χ is the angle between them, and α_1 and α_2 are the angles between the dipole axes and the line along which d is measured. This expression is easily transformed into one containing only *constant* geometrical quantities and the *variable* angle ϕ (cf. Fig. 24):

$$U=[\mu_1\mu_2/(K+B\cos\phi)^{5/2}][D_0+D_1\cos\phi+D_2\cos^2\phi].$$

Since in ethylene dichloride there are a number of dipoles, this equation is applied to these paired two at a time, the total energy is then obtained as the sum of

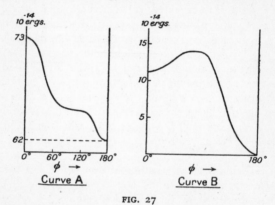

FIG. 27

nine energies. When plotted against ϕ this total energy varies as shown in the curve A. It is seen that the energy of a completely *cis* form is *ca.* $(73-62) \cdot 10^{-14}$ erg higher than that of the *trans* form—a ΔE not small in comparison with kT ($4 \cdot 1$ or $6 \cdot 2 \times 10^{-14}$ erg at $300°$ or $450°$ A.).

If ethylene dichloride is treated as a mixture of *cis* and *trans* forms, then the relative numbers of molecules in each configuration at any temperature should be calculable approximately as $n_1/n_2 = \exp(-\Delta E/kT)$. Such an equation foretells that a rise of temperature will increase the proportion of the molecules which are in higher energy levels, i.e. which have larger moments; this is in qualitative agreement both with the conclusions of Meyer and the results of experiment. The actual ΔE figure just quoted strongly favours *trans* configurations for the conditions under which $\mu_{apparent}$ has been measured. It is, however, perhaps relevant that published electron diffraction intensities are reconcilable with $Cl.CH_2.CH_2.Cl$ being in a state of oscillation about a *trans* model (Beach and Palmer, *J. Chem. Physics*, 1938, **6**, 639).

Lennard-Jones and Pike (*Trans. Far. Soc.*, 1934, **30**, 830) and Altar (*J. Chem. Physics*, 1935, **3**, 460) have proceeded differently from the above authors; the mutual potential energy being simply assumed to be some function of the azimuthal angle ϕ. Both treatments imply that electrostatic forces are not enough, alone, to explain the observed facts, Altar considering that in the special case of dichloroethane they do not make a contribution of more than a few hundred calories/mole and that the dominating forces arise from van der Waals attractions and steric repulsions. For these the potentials $U(\phi)$ must be estimated.

To this end, Lennard-Jones and Pike write U as $v_0(1+\cos\phi)$, and Altar as $U_1\cos\phi+U_2\cos 2\phi$. Further possible potential functions have since been examined by Beach and Stevenson (*J. Chem. Physics*, 1938, **6**, 635). Subsequent manipulation is similar in the three cases; e.g. Altar's equation is fitted to some set of experimental data—such as those of Zahn, giving the temperature variation of the mean square of the dipole moment—by solving for $U(\phi)$ the equation giving the mean value of

$$\overline{\cos\phi} = \frac{\int_0^{2\pi} \cos\phi \cdot e^{-U(\phi)/kT} \cdot d\phi}{\int_0^{2\pi} e^{-U(\phi)/kT} \cdot d\phi}.$$

This average cos ϕ is accessible because, for the structure specified in Fig. 24,

$$\bar{\mu}^2_{observed} = 2\mu^2(1 - \cos^2\theta + \sin^2\theta\,\overline{\cos\phi}).$$

The measurements cited give as the closest approximation: $U = (0.57\cos\phi - 0.34\cos 2\phi).10^{-13}$ erg. This is shown graphically in Curve B (Fig. 27). It differs considerably from the corresponding curve obtained by Smyth *et al.*, and shows a steep rise of potential from the *trans* position ($\phi = 180°$) up to *ca.* 130°, attributed to repulsion between either of the Cl atoms and the closer H atom belonging to the other group. Upon further approach to the *cis* position, however, the rate of increase of repulsion changes markedly; this the authors attribute to the possibility that here the repulsion is mainly that between the two bound Cl atoms—which can repel at much greater distances than have been usually assumed. The postulation of a high repulsive force between Cl and H atoms in such molecules is in accord with knowledge of the relative stabilities of the two isomers of dichloro-ethylene, Ebert and Büll (*Z. physikal. Chem.*, 1931, **152A,** 451) having found that the thermal equilibrium at 300° C. was 63 per cent *cis*: 37 per cent *trans*, although were electrostatic repulsions due to the two C—Cl dipoles alone considered in calculating the energies of these configurations, the relative stabilities would be the reverse, i.e. the *trans* form should be more stable and therefore occur in the greater proportion. The somewhat allied substance *sym*-tetrachloroethane, $CHCl_2 . CHCl_2$, has been stated by Langseth and Bernstein (*J. Chem. Physics*, 1940, **8,** 410) to behave as though composed of a *cis* form and two spectroscopically undistinguishable species intermediate between *cis* and *trans*. Evidently interactions more important than those between dipoles are operative and a potential energy $-\phi$ curve with three minima is to be inferred.

To conclude, therefore, disentanglement of the various factors influencing the configurations of molecules built around 'single' links is complicated and incomplete. In addition to obvious electrostatic and steric forces, there is often a possibility that through mesomerism the axial bond really has a single-double hybrid character (and with this an increased torsional rigidity); moreover, 'van der Waals' attractions between non-bonded parts of flexible molecules also need to be considered. These will tend to favour planar forms. The last two causes probably operate, for example, with the hindered $o:o'$-di-derivatives of diphenyl, for which at first glance the 'obstacle' properties of the *ortho*-groupings would appear alone sufficient to explain the inhibition of rotation (cf. Weissberger *et al.*, *Trans. Far. Soc.*, 1934, **30**, 884, papers quoted in *J.C.S.*, 1939, 1614, and the *Far. Soc.*, 1951 Discussion on 'Hydrocarbons'. *Re* 2:2'-dipyridyl, see Fielding and Le Fèvre, *J.C.S.*, 1951, 1811).

Finally, an additional possibility emerges when the twisting is studied of links other than C—C. For hydrogen peroxide and hydrazine rather large moments have been recorded (solution measurements) which would not be unreasonable if free rotation were to occur in the two molecules, H—O—O—H and NH_2—NH_2. Penney and Sutherland (*Trans. Far. Soc.*, 1934, **30**, 898), however, consider such an assumption unlikely to be true. They suggest that in the former case, the dominant factor in the relation between azimuthal angle ϕ and energy arises from the interaction of the electronic clouds on the oxygen atoms. These do not possess axial symmetry about the O—O line and as a result the position $\phi=90°$ is slightly more stable than the position $\phi=0°$ or $180°$. Similarly for hydrazine, the chief effect comes from the interactions between the electron clouds on the central atoms. Accordingly, the conclusion is

9*

drawn that these molecules are skew structures with the following specifications:

H_2O_2: H—O—O angles *ca.* 100°; azimuthal angle *ca.* 100°

N_2H_4: H—N—H angles *ca.* 110°; H—N—N angles *ca.* 110°

with planes containing the two N atoms and bisecting the two H—N—H angles perpendicular to each other. On these data and using the observed moments of H_2O and NH_3 the calculated moments (viz. H_2O_2, $2·0D$; N_2H_4, $1·70D$) are in good agreement with the experimentally obtained figures ($2·13D$ and $1·83D$) respectively.

DIPOLE MOMENTS AND NON-STRUCTURAL PROBLEMS

In the preceding pages attention has been directed deliberately towards those applications of polarity measurements which bear on molecular structure or configuration. Many more of high usefulness in other respects remain unmentioned. In particular, the author regrets that space will not allow a discussion of the fruitful relations that have emerged, e.g. between bond moments and the dissociation constants of acids (Waters, *Phil. Mag.*, 1929, viii, 436; Watson *et al.*, *J.C.S.*, 1933, 894; 1936, 438), or the energies of activation in chemical reactions (Waters, *J.C.S.*, 1933, 1551; Williams and Hinshelwood, *J.C.S.*, 1934, 1082; Watson, *Trans. Far. Soc.*, 1938, **34**, 165; Le Fèvre and Northcott, *J.C.S.*, 1949, 944). For such, and for a review of the more general role of dipole moments in the phenomena of reaction kinetics and mechanism, the reader may consult Moelwyn-Hughes (*Kinetics of Reactions in Solution*, 2nd edn., Oxford, 1947, Chaps. V and VII) in addition to the sources just cited.

GENERAL REFERENCES

Smyth, 'Electric Moment, Molecular Orientation and Structure in Aliphatic Compounds', *Chem. Revs.*, 1929, **6**, 549.

Williams, 'The Structure of Molecules as Revealed by Dielectric Constant Data', *ibid.*, 589

Sidgwick and Bowen, 'The Structure of Simple Molecules', *Annual Reps.*, 1931, **28**, 367

Richter, 'Recent Progress in Stereochemistry', *Chem. Revs.*, 1932, **10**, 365

Pauling, *The Nature of the Chemical Bond*, Cornell Univ. Press, 1945

Cottrell and Sutton, 'The Interpretation of Bond Properties', *Quarterly Revs.*, 1948, **2**, 260

Coulson, 'Representation of Simple Molecules by Molecular Orbitals', *ibid.*, 1947, **1**, 144

Crawford, 'Hyperconjugation', *ibid.*, 1949, **3**, 226

Bergmann and Weizmann, 'Dipole Moments as a Tool in the Determination of Structure', *Chem. Revs.*, 1942, **29**, 553

APPENDIX

TABLES OF DIPOLE MOMENTS

THE number of molecules for which dipole moments have been recorded is probably not far short of 3,000. Lists, each fairly complete to the year mentioned, are available as follow:

To 1933: *Trans. Far. Soc.*, 1934, **30**, appendix
To 1934: Landolt-Börnstein, *Tabellen*, 5th edn., Supplements IIa, 74, IIb, 969, IIIa, 117
To 1947: Wesson, 'Tables of Electric Dipole Moments', Technology Press, M.I.T., 1948

Where an individual substance is concerned there is often—as Sutton (*J.C.S.*, 1951, 2807) puts it—'a most troublesome degree of disagreement between the measurements of different investigators'. Sutton mentions six possible reasons for this and, in the consequential absence of *critical* tables, concludes that 'users of ordinary tables are obliged to exercise personal judgment or else to re-examine compounds themselves'. In the following short selection of moments (in Debye units), therefore, whenever the literature has offered a plurality of values in a given case, that figure is quoted *which seems to the present author* the most reliable. Determinations carried out in the *gas* phase are indicated by G, those in *solution* by the formula of the solvent employed; the method of calculation by which the moment was obtained is shown by T (temperature method), R (refractivity method), D (refractivity method but using the true $_DP$ instead of R), or S (Stark splitting). Older data (i.e. those not marked with an asterisk) require multiplication by 1·006 to adjust them to a basis involving the latest revisions of Avogadro's and Boltzmann's constants (see p. 14).

Inorganic Compounds

All elements	0	(various methods)	TiCl$_4$	0	(CCl$_4$; R)
LiClO$_4$	7·8	(C$_6$H$_6$O$_2$; R)	SnCl$_4$	0	(C$_6$H$_6$; R)
AgClO$_4$	10–12	(C$_6$H$_6$; R)	NH$_3$	1·45	(G; T)
BCl$_3$	0	(C$_6$H$_6$; R)	N$_2$H$_4$	1·84	(C$_6$H$_6$; R)
AsF$_3$	2·815	(S)	PF$_3$	1·025	(S)
AlBr$_3$	ca. 5	(C$_6$H$_6$; R)	PCl$_5$	0	(CCl$_4$; T)
	0·6	(CS$_2$; R)	H$_2$O	1·84	(G; T)*
SiH$_4$	0	(G; T)	H$_2$S	0·89	(G; T)*
SiCl$_4$	0	(CCl$_4$; R)	SF$_6$	0	(G; T)
HF	1·91	(G; T)	SO$_2$	1·62	(G; T)
HCl	1·08	(G; T)	NO	0·16	(G; T)
HBr	0·79	(G; T)	CO	0·12	(G; T)
HI	0·38	(G; T)	N$_2$O	0·166	(S)

Hydrocarbons

All saturated hydrocarbons	0	(various methods)	o-(CH$_3$)$_2$C$_6$H$_4$	0·6	(C$_6$H$_6$; R)
			m- ,,	0·4	(C$_6$H$_6$; R)
			p- ,,	0	(C$_6$H$_6$; R)
C$_2$H$_4$	0	(G; T)	C$_10$H$_8$	0	(C$_6$H$_6$; R)
C$_2$H$_2$	0	(G; T)	C$_6$H$_5$.C$_6$H$_5$	0	(C$_6$H$_6$; R)
CH$_3$CH:CH$_2$	0·34	(G; T)	Azulene	ca. 1	(C$_6$H$_6$; R)
C$_6$H$_6$	0	(various methods)			
C$_6$H$_5$CH$_3$	0·37	(G; T)			

Halogen Compounds

CH$_3$F	1·81	(G; T)	C$_6$H$_5$F	1·57	(G; T)
CH$_3$Cl	1·86	(G; T)*		1·48	(C$_6$H$_6$; R)*
	1·869	(S)	C$_6$H$_5$Cl	1·73	(G; T)*
CH$_3$Br	1·82	(G; T)*		1·59	(C$_6$H$_6$; R)*
	1·797	(S)	C$_6$H$_5$Br	1·71	(G; R)
CH$_3$I	1·64	(G; T)		1·57	(C$_6$H$_6$; R)*
	1·647	(S)	C$_6$H$_5$I	1·42	(C$_6$H$_6$; R)*
Higher alkyl halides, p. 95			Dihalogenoethylenes, p. 87		
CH$_2$Cl$_2$	1·57	(G; T)*	Ethylene dichloride, p. 122		
	1·55	(C$_6$H$_6$; D)*	C$_6$H$_4$CH$_2$Cl	2·04	(C$_6$H$_6$; R)
CHCl$_3$	1·01	(G; T)*	o:o'-Dichloro-		
	1·13	(C$_6$H$_6$; D)*	diphenyl	1·77	(C$_6$H$_6$; R)
Bromacetylene	0	(G; T)	m:m' ,,	1·68	(C$_6$H$_6$; R)
α-C$_{10}$H$_7$Cl	1·6	(C$_6$H$_6$; R)	p:p' ,,	0	(C$_6$H$_6$; R)
			β-C$_{10}$H$_7$Cl	1·7	(C$_6$H$_6$; R)

Hydroxylic Compounds

CH$_3$OH	1·68	(G; T)	C$_6$H$_5$CH$_2$OH	1·7	(C$_6$H$_6$; R)
	1·68	(C$_6$H$_6$; R)	α-Naphthol	1·4	(C$_6$H$_6$; R)
C$_2$H$_5$OH	1·70	(G; T)	β- ,,	1·5	(C$_6$H$_6$; R)
	1·74	(C$_6$H$_6$; R)	n-C$_7$H$_{15}$OH	1·71	(C$_6$H$_6$; R)
C$_6$H$_5$OH	1·7	(C$_6$H$_6$; R)	n-C$_8$H$_{17}$OH	1·70	(C$_6$H$_6$; R)
C$_6$H$_{11}$OH	1·7	(C$_6$H$_6$; R)	Cetyl alcohol	1·70	(C$_6$H$_6$; R)

Aldehydes and Ketones

CH$_3$CHO	2·72	(G; T)	C$_6$H$_5$.COCH$_3$	2·96	(C$_6$H$_6$; R)*
(CH$_3$)$_2$CO	ca. 2·9	(G; T)	Camphor	3·10	(C$_6$H$_6$; T)
	2·74	(C$_6$H$_6$; R)	(C$_6$H$_5$)$_2$CO	3·0	(C$_6$H$_6$; R)
(C$_3$H$_5$)$_2$CO	2·72	(C$_6$H$_6$; R)	Piperitone	3·75	(C$_6$H$_6$; R)
C$_6$H$_5$.CHO	2·98	(C$_6$H$_6$; R)*	The phthalaldehydes, p. 119		

Ethers

CH₃OCH₃	1·29	(G; T)*	C₆H₅OC₆H₅	1·17	(C₆H₆; R)
Ethylene oxide	1·89	(G; T)*	Catechol and quinol ethers, p. 119		
C₂H₅OC₂H₅	1·17	(G; T)*	Paraldehyde	1·44	(G; T)*
C₆H₅OCH₃	1·30	(C₆H₆; R)*	,,	ca. 2	(various
Furan	0·7	(C₆H₆; R)			solvents; R)
C₆H₅OC₆H₅	1·0	(C₆H₆; R)			

Acids and Esters

H.CO₂H	1·2	(C₆H₆; R)	H.COOC₃H₇	1·9	(C₆H₆; R)
H.CO₂C₂H₅	1·9	(C₆H₆; R)	CH₃.COOC₅H₇	1·9	(C₆H₆; R)
CH₃CO₂H	0·8	(C₆H₆; R)	Ethyl maleate and fumarate, p. 119		
CH₃CO₂H	1·23	(ether R)	Various optically active esters, p. 120		
CH₃.CO₂C₂H₅	1·86	(C₆H₆; R)	The dimethyl phthalates, p. 119		

Nitro Compounds

CH₃NO₂	3·0	(C₆H₆; R)	p-NO₂C₆H₄CHO	2·4	(C₆H₆; R)
CH₃CH₂NO₂	3·2	(C₆H₆; R)	p-NO₂C₆H₄CH₃	4·4	(C₆H₆; R)
C₆H₅NO₂	3·3	(C₆H₆; R)	p-NO₂C₆H₄NH₂	6·3	(C₆H₆; R)
C₆H₅NO₂	4·24	(G; T)*	p-NO₂C₆H₄CN	0·7	(C₆H₆; R)
	3·97	(C₆H₆; D)*	p-Cl.C₆H₄NO₂	2·6	(C₆H₆; R)
p-NO₂C₆H₄OH	5·03	(C₆H₆; R)	p-Br.C₆H₄NO₂	2·5	(C₆H₆; R)

Amines

CH₃NH₂	1·28	(G; T)	C₆H₅NHCH₃	1·67	(C₆H₆; R)*
(CH₃)₂NH	1·02	(G; T)	C₆H₅N(CH₃)₂	1·61	(C₆H₆; R)*
(CH₃)₃N	0·64	(G; T)	(C₆H₅)₃N	0·26	(C₆H₆; R)
C₂H₅NH₂	1·22	(G; T)*	p-(NH₂)₂C₆H₄	1·60	(C₆H₆; R)*
(C₂H₅)₂NH	0·92	(G; T)*	Benzidine	1·60	(C₆H₆; R)*
	1·06	(C₆H₆; R)*	p-(NO).C₆H₄.N(CH₃)₂	6·9	(C₆H₆; R)
C₆H₅NH₂	1·52	(C₆H₆; R)*	p-ClC₆H₄NH₂	3·0	(C₆H₆; R)
p-CH₃C₆H₄NH₂	1·52	(C₆H₆; R)*	p-ClC₆H₄N(CH₃)₂	3·29	(C₆H₆; R)

Other Nitrogen Compounds

CH₃CN	ca. 4·0	(G; T)	Phenazine	0	(C₆H₆; R)
C₂H₅CN	3·4	(C₆H₆; R)	Azobenzene (cis)	3·0	(C₆H₆; R)
Pyrrole	1·8	(C₆H₆; R)	,, (trans)	0	(C₆H₆; R)
Pyridine	2·2	(C₆H₆; R)	Benzocinnoline	3·9	(C₆H₆; R)
C₆H₅CN	4·05	(C₆H₆; R)	Nitrosobenzene	3·2	(C₆H₆; R)
C₆H₅NC	3·6	(C₆H₆; R)	Azoxybenzene	1·7	(C₆H₆; R)
C₆H₅CH₂CN	3·5	(C₆H₆; R)	,, (iso)	4·7	(C₆H₆; R)
Quinoline	2·2	(C₆H₆; R)	C₆H₅N₃	1·6	(C₆H₆; R)
Iso-Quinoline	2·5	(C₆H₆; R)	p-NO₂.C₆H₄.N₃	2·96	(C₆H₆; R)
Ar-diazocyanides, p. 110			(CH₂)₆N₄	0	(CHCl₃; R)

Sulphur Compounds

CS₂	0	(various	(C₂H₅)₂SO₂	4·41	(C₆H₆; R)
		methods)	C₆H₅.N:S:O	2·6	(C₆H₆; R)
COS	0·65	(G; T)	C₆H₅SH	1·33	(C₆H₆; R)
	0·7085	(S)	C₆H₅.N:C:S	3·0	(C₆H₆; R)
C₂H₅SH	1·39	(C₆H₆; R)	C₆H₅.S.C:N	3·6	(C₆H₆; R)
CH₃SCH₃	1·40	(C₆H₆; R)	Thianthren	1·57	(C₆H₆; R)
C₃H₅.N:C:S	3·31	(C₆H₆; R)	C₆H₅.S.C₆H₅	1·5	(C₆H₆; R)
C₃H₅.S:C:N	3·64	(C₆H₆; R)	(C₆H₅)₂SO	4·1	(C₆H₆; R)
Thiophen	0·6	(C₆H₆; R)	(C₆H₅)₂SO₂	5·1	(C₆H₆; R)
C₂H₅.S.C₂H₅	1·6	(C₆H₆; R)			

Miscellaneous Compounds

$C_6H_5.Se.C_6H_5$	1·4	$(C_6H_6; R)$	$(C_6H_5)_3As$	1·07 $(C_6H_6; R)$
$C_6H_5.Te.C_6H_5$	1·1	$(C_6H_6; R)$	$(C_6H_5)_3Sb$	0·57 $(C_6H_6; R)$
Selanthren	1·41	$(C_6H_6; R)$	$(C_6H_5)_3Bi$	ca. 0 $(C_6H_6; R)$
$(C_6H_5)_2Hg$	0·5	(dekalin; R)	Et_3SnCl	3·4 $(CCl_4; R)$
$(C_6H_5)_3P$	1·45	$(C_6H_6; R)$	Et_3SiCl	2·1 $(CCl_4; R)$
CH_3SnH_3	0·68	(S)	Ph_3GeBr	2·35 $(C_6H_6; R)$

(Cf. also data tabulated or mentioned on pp. 22, 31, 63, 64, 66, 75, 77, 83, 85, 95, 101, 102, 105, 106, 108, 110–118, and 130.)

INDEX